ENERGY POLICIES, POLITICS AND PRICES

DEMAND-RESPONSE IN THE UNITED STATES

EXPANSION EFFORTS AND ELECTRICITY MARKET ACTIVITIES

ENERGY POLICIES, POLITICS AND PRICES

Additional books in this series can be found on Nova's website under the Series tab.

Additional e-books in this series can be found on Nova's website under the e-book tab.

ENERGY POLICIES, POLITICS AND PRICES

DEMAND-RESPONSE IN THE UNITED STATES

EXPANSION EFFORTS AND ELECTRICITY MARKET ACTIVITIES

CARINA REILLY
EDITOR

New York

For permission to use material from this book please contact us:
Telephone 631-231-7269; Fax 631-231-8175
Web Site: http://www.novapublishers.com

Library of Congress Cataloging-in-Publication Data

ISBN: 978-1-63321-576-4

Published by Nova Science Publishers, Inc. † New York

CONTENTS

PREFACE

Since 2004, the federal government has made efforts to facilitate demand-response activities, including expanding their use in wholesale electricity markets. Among these efforts, the Federal Energy Regulatory Commission (FERC) issued regulatory orders affecting Regional Transmission Organizations (RTO)—entities that operate the transmission system and administer wholesale markets in some parts of the country. For example, FERC issued orders approving RTO rules for quantifying the extent of demand-response activities and compensating consumers for their demand-response activities. This book provides an update since 2004 and discusses federal efforts to facilitate demand-response activities; FERC efforts to collect and report data on demand response activities; changes in the extent of demand-response activities; key benefits and challenges of current efforts.

Chapter 1 – Electricity demand fluctuates throughout the day and year and, as GAO has reported, electricity is generated first at U.S. power plants with the lowest operating costs, and, as demand rises, at more costly plants. Prior to being sold to retail consumers such as households and businesses, electricity is traded in wholesale markets. Regulation of electricity markets is divided; states oversee retail markets, and FERC oversees wholesale markets. In 2004, GAO reported on the benefits of encouraging consumers to reduce demand when the cost to generate electricity is high. These activities are known as "demand-response activities," which can reduce the costs of producing electricity, improve market functions, and enhance reliability.

GAO was asked to examine demand-response activities. This report provides an update since 2004 and discusses: (1) federal efforts to facilitate demand-response activities, (2) FERC efforts to collect and report data on demand-response activities, (3) changes in the extent of demand-response activities, and (4) key benefits and challenges of current efforts. GAO reviewed documents and conducted interviews with government officials and industry stakeholders with demand-response expertise.

Chapter 2 – The efficient and reliable functioning of the more than $200 billion electric industry is vital to the lives of all Americans. As demonstrated in the 2003 black- out in the Northeast and the 2001 energy crisis in the West, changes in the cost and availability of electricity can have significant impacts on consumers and the national economy. The Federal Energy Regulatory Commission (FERC) supports using demand-response programs as part of its effort to develop and oversee competitive electricity markets.

GAO was asked to identify (1) the types of demand-response programs currently in use, (2) the benefits of these programs, (3) the barriers to their introduction and expansion, and (4) instances where barriers have been overcome. Additionally, GAO examined the federal government's participation in these programs through the General Services Administration (GSA).

Chapter 3 – This report is the Federal Energy Regulatory Commission staff's (Commission staff's) eighth annual report on demand response and advanced metering. It fulfills a requirement of the Energy Policy Act of 2005 (EPAct 2005) section 1252(e)(3) that the Federal Energy Regulatory Commission (FERC or Commission) prepare and publish an annual report, by appropriate region, that assesses electricity demand response resources, including those available from all consumer classes.

In: Demand-Response in the United States
Editor: Carina Reilly
ISBN: 978-1-63321-576-4

Chapter 1

ELECTRICITY MARKETS: DEMAND-RESPONSE ACTIVITIES HAVE INCREASED, BUT FERC COULD IMPROVE DATA COLLECTION AND REPORTING EFFORTS*

United States Government Accountability Office

WHY GAO DID THIS STUDY

Electricity demand fluctuates throughout the day and year and, as GAO has reported, electricity is generated first at U.S. power plants with the lowest operating costs, and, as demand rises, at more costly plants. Prior to being sold to retail consumers such as households and businesses, electricity is traded in wholesale markets. Regulation of electricity markets is divided; states oversee retail markets, and FERC oversees wholesale markets. In 2004, GAO reported on the benefits of encouraging consumers to reduce demand when the cost to generate electricity is high. These activities are known as "demand-response activities," which can reduce the costs of producing electricity, improve market functions, and enhance reliability.

---

* This is an edited, reformatted and augmented version of a United States Government Accountability Office publication, No. GAO-14-73, dated March 2014.

GAO was asked to examine demand-response activities. This report provides an update since 2004 and discusses: (1) federal efforts to facilitate demand-response activities, (2) FERC efforts to collect and report data on demand-response activities, (3) changes in the extent of demand-response activities, and (4) key benefits and challenges of current efforts. GAO reviewed documents and conducted interviews with government officials and industry stakeholders with demand-response expertise.

What GAO Recommends

GAO recommends FERC review the scope of its data collection and improve the transparency of its reporting efforts. In commenting on a draft of this report, FERC stated that it would take the report's recommendations and findings under advisement. GAO believes in the importance of fully implementing these recommendations.

What GAO Found

Since 2004, the federal government has made efforts to facilitate demand-response activities, including expanding their use in wholesale electricity markets. Among these efforts, the Federal Energy Regulatory Commission (FERC) issued regulatory orders affecting Regional Transmission Organizations (RTO)—entities that operate the transmission system and administer wholesale markets in some parts of the country. For example, FERC issued orders approving RTO rules for quantifying the extent of demand-response activities and compensating consumers for their demand-response activities.

FERC collects and reports data on demand-response activities in accordance with the Energy Policy Act of 2005, but these efforts have limitations. Electricity markets and demand-response activities have changed since FERC began collecting and reporting this data in 2006, but FERC has not reviewed the scope of its efforts to determine whether they could better reflect changes in electricity markets and demand-response activities. For example, FERC has reported that the limited number of retail consumers paying rates that vary with the cost of serving them is a barrier to expanding demand-response activities, but its report provides limited data on the number of consumers doing so. GAO has reported that evaluation of programs or efforts with a specific focus—such as FERC's demand-response data collection efforts—can play a key role in management and oversight. FERC, in some cases, adjusts the data it collects before making them available to the public—using its judgment to improve the data's consistency, for example—but does not fully document these adjustments. Best practices for data management advise that data modifications be documented. By not addressing these limitations, FERC is missing opportunities to make its data more informative and transparent to users for analysis of trends in demand-response activities and the extent to which progress has been made in addressing barriers.

Since GAO's 2004 report, FERC data show that the extent of demand-response activities has increased, with demand-response activities in wholesale and retail markets more than doubling from a total of 29,653 megawatts (MW) of potential reduction in peak demand in 2005 to more than 66,350 MW in 2011—about 8.5 percent of total peak demand. Demand-response activities in retail markets have increased 81 percent from a reported 20,754 MW of potential reduction in 2005 to a reported 37,543 MW in 2011. In wholesale markets, demand-response activities more than tripled from 2005 through 2011—increasing from 8,899 MW of potential reduction in 2005 to 28,807 MW of potential reduction in 2011—but the extent of demand-response activities has varied by RTO region.

According to stakeholders, current demand-response efforts provide benefits for consumers, including increasing reliability and lowering prices, but these efforts also pose a number of challenges for wholesale markets. For example, FERC's efforts to encourage demand-response activities in the markets it oversees have made these markets more complex by introducing administrative functions that, according to stakeholders, have led to challenges. Challenges include the need to develop estimates of the amount of electricity a consumer would have used in order to quantify the reduction in electricity use from demand-response activities. FERC has taken some steps to address these challenges, but it is too soon to tell whether these steps will be effective.

ABBREVIATIONS

DOE	Department of Energy
EIA	Energy Information Administration

EPA	Environmental Protection Agency
ERCOT	Electric Reliability Council of Texas
FERC	Federal Energy Regulatory Commission
GW	gigawatt
ISO	Independent System Operator
MW	megawatt
NERC	North American Electric Reliability Corporation
PURPA	Public Utility Regulatory Policies Act of 1978
RTO	Regional Transmission Organization

March 27, 2014

The Honorable Thomas R. Carper
Chairman
Committee on Homeland Security and Governmental Affairs
United States Senate

The Honorable Susan M. Collins
United States Senate

The Honorable Peter Welch
House of Representatives

Electricity is vital to the nation's economy and central to the lives of all Americans. Businesses—from large industrial manufacturers to small businesses—rely on electricity to produce trillions of dollars in products and services. Residential consumers rely on electricity to power household appliances and other devices important to their daily lives.[1] Given its importance, the price and reliability of electricity can have substantial impacts on consumers and the broader economy.

Electricity is supplied through a complex network of power plants and power lines—the electricity grid—managed by utility companies and other operators. Since electricity cannot be easily stored, power plants' electricity output must be matched precisely with demand, which varies significantly depending on the time of day and year. To maintain a reliable supply of electricity, operators of the electricity grid take steps to ensure that power plants will be available to generate electricity when needed. In doing so, they typically ensure availability exceeds estimated demand so that any unexpected increases in demand or power plant outages can be accommodated without consumers losing access to electricity. As demand for electricity varies throughout the day and year, grid operators respond by continually increasing or decreasing the amount of electricity that they call upon power plants to generate. As we have previously reported, the cost of generating electricity varies, and grid operators generally rely on plants that are the least costly to operate first and most often and plants that are the most costly to operate last and least often.[2] Because the plants used to meet the highest levels of demand are generally much more expensive to operate, there is significant variation in the costs of serving consumers throughout the day and year.

Responsibility for regulating electricity is divided between states and the federal government. Most electricity consumers are served by retail markets that are regulated by the states, generally through state public utility commissions or equivalent organizations. As the primary regulator of retail markets, state commissions approve many aspects of utility operations, such as the siting and construction of new power plants, as well as the prices consumers pay and how those prices are set. [3] In 2004, we reported that most retail consumers paid electricity prices that reflected the average cost of serving them for an extended period.[4] Such extended periods could be a year or longer. Prior to being sold to these retail consumers, such as households and businesses, electricity is bought, sold, and traded in wholesale electricity markets by companies that own power plants, as well as utilities and other companies that sell electricity directly to retail consumers. Wholesale buyers may purchase electricity at prices that vary throughout the day and year and are largely determined by the interaction of supply and demand. Wholesale electricity markets are regulated by the federal government. The Federal Energy Regulatory Commission (FERC), which oversees wholesale electricity sales, among other things, has statutory responsibility to ensure that wholesale electricity rates are "just and reasonable" and not "unduly discriminatory or preferential."[5] Historically, FERC met this responsibility by approving electricity rates based on utilities' costs of production plus a rate-of-return that it determined to be reasonable. Beginning in the late 1990s, FERC took a series of significant steps to restructure the wholesale electricity markets to increase the role of competition—market forces of supply and demand—in setting prices.[6]

We previously reported that, while regulation of retail and wholesale markets is divided, these markets are interconnected and operationally joined, with generation and consumption of electricity separated by milliseconds.[7] We also reported that encouraging consumers to change their demand for electricity in response to changes in varying prices and the availability of other incentives can offer cost savings and operating advantages over relying solely upon increases in the production of electricity to meet demand. These activities are collectively known as “demand-response activities,” and they can be integrated into both retail and wholesale markets. For example, to encourage retail consumers to reduce demand when costs are high, such as on summer afternoons, utilities may charge prices that vary throughout the day and year to reflect the costs of serving consumers. Alternatively, utilities may provide consumers with financial or other incentives to install technologies on certain equipment—such as pool pumps, air conditioners, and water heaters—that allow the utility to directly lower electricity consumption of these devices during times of high demand. Similarly, in wholesale markets, grid operators may provide compensation to consumers for actions they take to use less electricity than expected during periods of peak demand.[8]

Our August 2004 report found that demand-response activities could benefit consumers by improving market functions and enhancing the reliability of the electricity system (e.g., the ability to meet consumers’ electricity demand).[9] We also found that such demand-response activities could encourage consumers to reduce demand when the cost to generate electricity is high. However, we highlighted three main barriers to expanding demand-response activities: (1) state regulations that shield consumers from short-term variations in the cost of producing electricity or wholesale prices; (2) the absence of equipment required for participation in demand-response programs at consumers’ sites, such as advanced meters that can measure electricity consumption on a more frequent basis;[10] and (3) consumers’ limited awareness of demand-response programs and their potential benefits. In 2005, through the Energy Policy Act, Congress encouraged time-based pricing of electricity—prices that vary with the cost of serving electricity consumers—and other forms of demand-response activities.[11] The act also provides that it is the policy of the United States that the deployment of technology and devices that enable electricity consumers to participate in such pricing and demand-response programs are to be facilitated, and that unnecessary barriers to expanding demand-response activities in electricity markets are to be eliminated. In addition, the act required that FERC prepare and publish an annual report that assesses demand-response resources in the United States. Additionally, we reported in 2012 that 2 to 12 percent of coal-fueled capacity may be retired and other plants may be modified to reduce environmental impacts and that demand-response could provide a way to mitigate potential reliability impacts of these actions.[12]

In this context, you asked us to examine U.S. efforts to expand demand-response activities. This report provides an update on the status of demand-response activities since we reported on them in 2004 and assesses: (1) the federal government's efforts to facilitate demand-response activities; (2) FERC efforts to collect and report data on demand-response activities; (3) changes, if any, in the extent of demand-response activities in retail and wholesale markets; and (4) key benefits and challenges, if any, of current demand-response efforts.

To do this work, we reviewed federal demand-response policies and interviewed officials from FERC, the Environmental Protection Agency (EPA), and the Department of Energy (DOE). In addition, we reviewed FERC demand-response data about how overall levels of demand-response activities have changed over time. We also analyzed data from a 2012 FERC survey of utility demand-response activities to identify the primary demand-response approaches in use at the retail level. To assess the reliability of these data, we interviewed FERC officials and performed electronic testing of the data. We found some elements of the data to be sufficiently reliable for our purposes. In other cases, we were unable to determine the quality of the data and, therefore, did not include related analyses in our report. In addition, we reviewed current literature, including reports about demand-response activities. We also interviewed a nonprobability sample of 37 electricity stakeholders with expertise on demand-response activities from trade associations and public interest organizations, academics and consultants, state government officials, industry representatives, and grid operators. We selected these five types of stakeholders to represent different perspectives on demand-response activities. Within each stakeholder group, we spoke with a diverse set of stakeholders to maintain balance on key issues—for example, their views on how to compensate those who participate in demand-response activities. Because this was a nonprobability sample, the information and perspectives that we obtained from the interviews are not generalizable to similar groups of stakeholders. We also interviewed an additional 5 stakeholders who had specialized knowledge about certain aspects of the electricity industry relevant to our study—for example, experience evaluating the competitiveness of the FERC-regulated wholesale markets. A more complete discussion of our objectives, scope, and methodology is provided in appendix I of this report.

We conducted this performance audit from September 2012 to March 2014 in accordance with generally accepted government auditing standards. Those standards require that we plan and perform the audit to obtain sufficient, appropriate evidence to provide a reasonable basis for our findings and conclusions based on our audit objectives. We believe that the evidence obtained provides a reasonable basis for our findings and conclusions based on our audit objectives.

BACKGROUND

This section describes (1) the balancing of supply and demand in regional electricity systems, (2) restructuring of the electricity sector and the expanding role of competition in markets, and (3) two key demand-response approaches.

Balancing Supply and Demand in Regional Electricity Systems

The electricity industry includes four distinct functions: generation, transmission, distribution, and system operations (see fig. 1). Electricity may be generated at power plants by burning fossil fuels; through nuclear fission; or by harnessing wind, solar, geothermal, or hydroenergy. Once electricity is generated, it is sent through the electricity grid, which consists of high-voltage, high-capacity transmission systems to areas where it is transformed to a lower voltage and sent through the local distribution system for use by business and residential consumers. Throughout this process, a grid operator, such as a local utility, must constantly balance the generation and consumption of electricity. To do so, grid operators monitor electricity consumption from a centralized location using computerized systems and send minute-by-minute signals to power plants to adjust their output to match changes in the demand for electricity.

Balancing the generation and consumption of electricity is challenging for grid operators because consumers use sharply different amounts of electricity through the course of the day and year. Although there are regional variations, demand typically rises through the day and reaches its highest point—called the peak—in late afternoon or early evening. In some parts of the country, average hourly demand can be up to twice as high during late afternoon and early evening as it is during the middle of the night and early morning hours. In addition to these daily variations in demand, electricity demand varies seasonally, mainly because air-conditioning during the summer accounts for a large share of overall electricity usage in many parts of the country. In some areas, peak usage can be twice as high during the summer as it is during the winter.

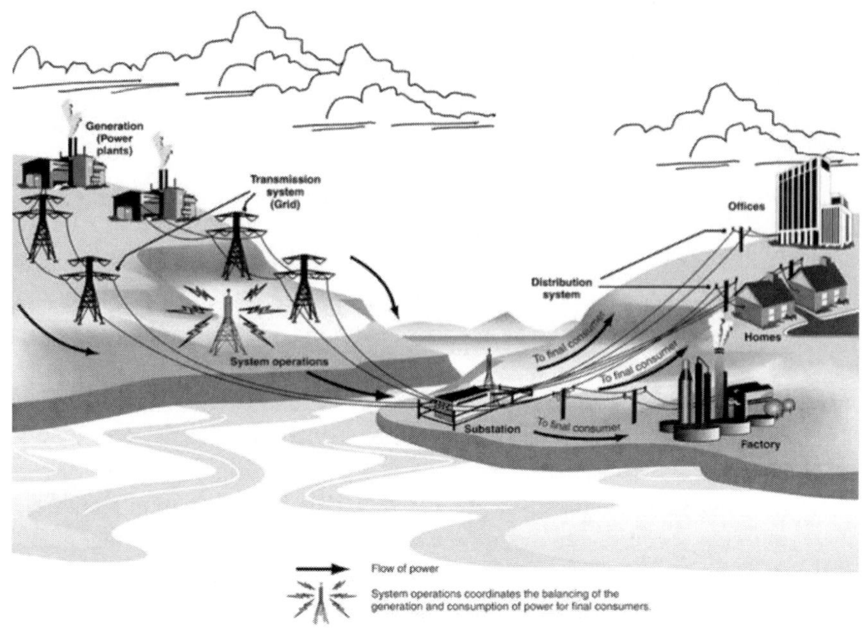

Source: GAO.

Figure 1. Functions of the Electricity Industry.

The power plants that grid operators use to meet this varying demand include baseload plants and peakers. Baseload plants are generally the most costly to build but have the lowest hourly operating costs.[13] In general, grid operators maximize the amount of electricity supplied by the baseload plants, which are often used continuously for long periods of time. As demand rises through the day and through the year and exceeds the amount of electricity generation that can be delivered from baseload power plants, grid operators increasingly rely on electricity supplied by peakers. Peakers are usually less costly to build but more costly to operate.[14]

As grid operators' reliance on peakers rises, the cost of meeting demand can increase considerably. For example, the wholesale price of electricity can rise almost 10-fold in the late afternoon and early evening, when demand is at its highest and more peakers are being utilized, compared to nighttime and early morning, when demand is at its lowest and few, if any, peakers are being utilized. Peak periods are generally short and account for only a few hours per day and, overall, a small percentage of the hours during a year, but can significantly contribute to the overall costs of serving consumers.

According to a 2012 report by DOE's Lawrence Berkeley National Laboratory, spikes in demand during peak periods have a significant economic impact.[15] This report estimates that, in many electricity systems, 10 percent or more of the costs of generating electricity are incurred to meet levels of demand that occur less than 1 percent of the time.

Maintaining a reliable supply of electricity is a complex process requiring the grid operator to coordinate three broad types of services as follows:

- **Energy**. Operators schedule which power plants will produce electricity—referred to as energy scheduling—to maintain the balance of electricity generation and consumption. As a general rule, grid operators will schedule the least costly baseload power plants first and run them longest, and schedule the most costly peaker plants last and run them less often.
- **Capacity**. Operators procure capacity—long-term commitments to provide specific amounts of electricity generation to ensure that there will be sufficient electricity to reliably meet consumers' expected future electricity needs. Procuring capacity may involve operators of power plants committing that existing or new power plants will be available to generate electricity, if needed, at a particular future date. To provide for potential unexpected increases in demand or any problems that prevent some power plants from providing electricity or transmission lines from delivering electricity as expected, the commitments to provide electricity may exceed expected demand by a specified percentage or safety margin.
- **Ancillary services**. Operators procure several ancillary services to maintain a reliable electricity supply. Ancillary services encompass several highly technical functions required for grid operators to ensure that electricity produced can be delivered and used by consumers. Some ancillary services help ensure that electricity can be delivered within technical standards—for example, at the right voltage and frequency—to keep the grid stable and be useful for consumers who may have equipment that needs to operate at specific voltage and frequency levels.

Restructuring of the Electricity Sector and the Expanding Role of Competition and Markets

Over the last 2 decades, some states and the federal government have taken steps to restructure the regulation of their electric systems with the goals of increasing the roles of competition in markets, lowering prices, and giving consumers access to a wider array of services. The electricity industry was historically characterized by integrated utilities that oversaw the four functions of electricity service—generation, transmission, distribution, and system operations—in a monopoly service territory in exchange for providing consumers with electricity at regulated retail prices. In certain parts of the country, states and the federal government restructured the electricity industry to one in which the wholesale price for electricity generation is determined largely by supply and demand in competitive markets. More specifically, historically, at the retail level, integrated monopoly utilities provided consumers with electricity at regulated prices, and state regulators generally set retail electricity prices based on a utility's cost of production plus a fair rate of return on the utility's investment in its infrastructure, including power plants and power lines. However, beginning in the late 1990s, some states chose to restructure the retail markets they oversee to allow the price of electricity to be determined largely by supply and demand in competitive markets. In parts of the country where electricity markets have restructured, new entities called retail service providers compete with existing utilities to provide electricity to consumers by offering electricity plans with differing prices, terms, and incentives.

At the wholesale level, FERC is required by law to ensure that the rates it oversees are "just and reasonable" and not "unduly discriminatory or preferential," among other things.[16] Prior to restructuring the wholesale electricity markets in the late 1990s, FERC met this requirement by approving rates for transmission and wholesale sales of electricity in interstate commerce based on the utilities' costs of production plus a fair rate of return on the utilities' investment.[17] After restructuring wholesale electricity markets, FERC continued to develop transmission rates in this same way. In addition, FERC provided authority for many entities—for example, independent owners of power plants—to sell electricity at prices determined by supply and demand where FERC determined that the markets were sufficiently competitive or that adequate procedures were in place to mitigate the effect of companies with a large market share and the ability to significantly control or affect prices in the markets. As a result, these entities can now compete with existing utilities and one another to sell electricity in wholesale markets.

As part of this restructuring process, FERC also encouraged the voluntary creation of new entities called Regional Transmission Organizations (RTO) to manage regional networks of electric transmission lines as grid operators—functions that, in these areas, had traditionally been carried out by local utilities.[18] Figure 2 indicates the location of major RTOs that have developed in certain regions of the United States. As grid operators, RTOs are responsible for managing transmission in their regions, which includes establishing and implementing rules and pricing related to transmission, as well as considering factors, such as weather conditions and equipment outages, that could affect the reliability of electricity supply and demand.[19]

Source: ISO/Regional Transmission Organization Council (data); Map Resources (map).

Note: This graphic reflects RTO borders based on available information as of February 2014, but these borders may change as territory is added or subtracted from RTO regions. The transmission grid that the Electric Reliability Council of Texas (ERCOT) administers is located solely within the state of Texas and constitutes a separate grid from the two other main grids in the continental United States. As a result, ERCOT is largely unregulated by FERC and is instead subject to oversight by the Public Utility Commission of Texas. ERCOT performs similar functions as the RTOs in this map, including managing Texas' transmission system and overseeing wholesale sales of electricity.

Figure 2. United States Regional Transmission Organizations (RTO).

Like other grid operators, such as utilities, RTOs take steps to schedule and procure energy, capacity, and ancillary services. RTOs often do so using the three broad types of markets they manage—energy markets; capacity markets; and markets for several different ancillary services, including voltage support and frequency support. In the energy markets, for example, sellers—such as owners of power plants—place offers with RTOs to supply an amount of electricity at a specific price. Potential buyers of this electricity, such as retail service providers, also place bids with RTOs defining their willingness to pay for it. RTOs periodically— hourly, for example—"stack" the offers to supply electricity from lowest offered price to highest until the RTO estimates that it has sufficient electricity to meet the total demand. The market clearing price, or the highest supply bid needed to satisfy the last unit of demand, is paid for each unit of electricity produced for that time period. Regions with RTOs are referred to as having "organized wholesale markets," because the RTOs centrally coordinate these transactions between buyers and sellers according to rules the RTOs have established and FERC has approved.

In regions of the country without RTOs, electric utilities generally continue to serve the role of grid operator. In these regions, the local utility often integrates the delivery of electricity services—energy to maintain the balance of electricity generation and consumption, capacity to meet demand and provide a safety margin, and a range of ancillary services. Utilities in these regions may build and operate power plants to provide electricity to serve their retail customers. These utilities may also buy electricity from other power plant owners.

Two Key Demand-Response Approaches

According to a 2006 FERC report on utilities' demand-response activities, programs focused on reducing consumer demand for electricity as part of grid operators' and utilities' efforts to balance supply and demand have been in place for decades.[20] FERC reported that demand-response activities—known as load management or demand-side management— increased markedly in the 1980s and early 1990s. This increase was driven by a combination of a directive in the Public Utility Regulatory Policies Act of 1978 (PURPA) to examine standards for time-based pricing and by state and federal policy focused on managing consumer demand and planning future resource availability for providing electricity.[21] However, according to data from NERC, estimates of certain demand-response activities generally declined between 1998 and 2003, just as FERC was beginning to restructure wholesale electricity markets.

Demand-response activities may occur within both retail and wholesale markets. The actions taken by retail and wholesale demand-response program participants are often not substantially different and typically involve consumers reducing their electricity consumption by delaying or stopping the use of electricity-consuming appliances, processes, or machinery during periods of high demand. As with electricity prices, FERC and state regulators each have interest in and responsibility for overseeing aspects of these demand-response activities, at the wholesale and retail levels, respectively.

There are two broad approaches to demand-response: (1) consumer-initiated and (2) operator-initiated. Specifically, these approaches are as follows:

- **Consumer-initiated approaches**. With consumer-initiated demand-response approaches, consumers determine when they will take specific actions to reduce the amount of electricity they consume. There are various types of consumer-initiated demand-response approaches. For example, retail consumers may pay time-based prices that vary with the cost of serving them with the goal of encouraging them to choose to reduce their use of electricity when prices are high.[22] Time-based prices include time-of-use prices, which vary at broad intervals, such as peak and off-peak times, and real-time prices, which vary at least hourly in response to changes in market conditions such as the cost of producing electricity at that time. Consumers' actions to reduce demand may be manual—such as turning off lights or delaying use of the clothes dryer—or automatic— such as using thermostats or other automated systems that are preprogrammed to reduce air conditioning use when prices reach a certain level. To participate in programs that use consumer-initiated approaches, consumers may need access to certain technology, such as the internet or a home display that provides information about changing prices. In addition, they may need a type of electric meter known as an advanced meter, which measures and records data on consumers' electricity use at closer intervals than standard electricity meter—typically at least hourly—and provides these data to both consumers and electricity suppliers.
- **Operator-initiated approaches**. Operator-initiated approaches allow grid operators to call on participating consumers to reduce demand—

for example, by shutting down equipment—during periods of tight supply in exchange for a payment or other financial incentive. These approaches can minimize the number of consumers losing access to electricity during periods of extremely high demand, reduce stress on a distribution network, or help accommodate the unexpected shut down of a power plant or transmission line. Incentives for participation in these approaches may include a payment, a bill credit, or a lower electricity price. Although participation in programs that use these approaches is typically voluntary, participating consumers may incur financial penalties if they do not reduce demand as they agreed to.

THE FEDERAL GOVERNMENT HAS MADE EFFORTS TO FACILITATE DEMAND-RESPONSE ACTIVITIES, INCLUDING EXPANDING THEIR USE IN WHOLESALE MARKETS

Since 2004, the federal government has undertaken efforts to facilitate demand-response activities. These efforts include actions to address barriers to expanding demand-response activities by funding the installation of advanced meters and facilitating coordination between FERC and state regulators. In addition, FERC has undertaken efforts to remove barriers to expanding, as well as encouraging consideration of demand-response activities in wholesale markets by approving the use of various demand-response approaches in individual RTO markets it regulates and, more recently, taking steps to establish more consistent rules for all RTOs.

DOE and FERC Have Taken Certain Actions to Help Address Barriers to Expanding Demand-Response Activities

DOE, which formulates national energy policy and funds research and development on various energy-related technologies, among other things, has taken a key step to address one barrier we identified in our 2004 report—the lack of advanced meters.[23] Specifically, in 2010, DOE began providing $3.4 billion in funds appropriated under the 2009 American Recovery and Reinvestment Act to install, among other things, advanced meters, communications systems, and programmable thermostats in homes, businesses, and other locations where electricity is used. Recipients of these DOE funds, such as utilities, provided additional funding to total $7.9 billion of investment. In recent years, the installation of advanced meters has grown substantially. Data from FERC indicate that the installation of advanced meters as a percentage of total meters installed has grown from 0.7 percent in 2005 to 22.9 percent in 2011.[24]

FERC has also taken action to collaborate with state regulators on demand-response policies, best practices, and other issues. In 2004, we noted the importance of FERC continuing to work with grid operators, RTOs, and interested state commissions, among others, to develop compatible policies regarding demand-response activities.[25] In 2006, FERC and the state public utility commissions—through the National Association of Regulatory Utility Commissioners[26]—took steps to coordinate their regulatory activities through a joint collaborative. This collaborative explored how federal and state regulators can better coordinate their respective approaches to demand-response policies and practices. In 2013, the focus of this collaborative was broadened to include additional topics that cut across the retail and wholesale electricity sectors to build more understanding between and amongst regulators.

In addition to their steps to address these barriers, FERC and DOE also took a series of steps to study how the federal government could encourage demand-response activities. The Energy Independence and Security Act of 2007 directed FERC to conduct a national assessment of demand-response potential, develop a national action plan on demand-response activities, and with DOE, develop a proposal to implement the National Action Plan.[27] FERC completed *A National Assessment of Demand Response Potential* in 2009 and identified significant potential for demand-response activities to reduce peak energy demand under several different scenarios. Under one scenario, called the "full participation scenario," FERC estimated that peak demand could be reduced by 188 gigawatts (GW)[28] compared with a scenario with no demand-response activities within 10 years.[29] This reduction is equal to approximately 2,500 peaking power plants.[30] The national assessment also identified remaining barriers to the adoption of demand-response approaches—such as the divided federal and state oversight responsibilities and the absence of a direct connection between wholesale and retail prices. In 2010, FERC completed its *National Action Plan on Demand Response*, which identified proposed activities and strategies for demand-response approaches across three broad areas: assistance to the states, national communications, and providing tools and materials.[31] One proposed action—the national communications program—has objectives focused on increasing consumer awareness and understanding of energy-consuming behavior and demand-response activities. FERC and DOE jointly completed the *Implementation Proposal for the National Action Plan on Demand Response*, identifying specific roles for DOE, FERC, and other entities. For example, DOE and FERC agreed to provide support for informational and educational sessions for regulators and policymakers.

FERC Has Approved the Use of More Demand-Response Activities in RTO Markets

Since we last reported in 2004, FERC has formally acknowledged that demand-response activities are important in electricity markets in general and in particular, in wholesale markets overseen by RTOs.[32] FERC has also reported that electricity markets are more effective when retail rates vary with the cost of serving consumers.[33] However, as retail markets are generally outside the scope of its authority, FERC historically focused its efforts on remaining barriers to participation of demand-response and encouraging RTOs to identify how demand-response activities could be incorporated into the wholesale markets they operate.[34] FERC has found that demand-response activities directly affect wholesale electricity prices; therefore, facilitating demand-response activities is essential to FERC fulfilling its responsibility for ensuring wholesale prices are just and reasonable.[35]

Since 2004, FERC has taken steps to remove barriers to further expand demand-response activities in RTO markets. Prior to our 2004 report, FERC had approved a few demand-response programs coordinated by the RTOs, but, as we reported, demand-response activities were in limited use.[36] Since our report was issued in 2004, individual RTOs have continued to develop opportunities for demand-response resources to provide specific services (e.g., energy, capacity, and ancillary services) through the markets they operate. According to FERC officials, FERC has reviewed these proposals on a case-by-case basis and, when FERC believed it to be appropriate, approved them. FERC has also addressed demand-response activities in broad orders related to other electricity regulation topics.[37]

As a result of FERC's approval of changes to individual RTOs' market rules, RTOs have utilized demand-response resources provided by various entities including both large electricity consumers and intermediaries. For example, demand-response resources may be provided directly by large consumers such as steel mills or other manufacturing facilities that purchase electricity directly from wholesale markets. These large consumers may delay the use of highly electricity intensive equipment, such as an electric arc furnace used to melt steel, until later in the day than they had planned in exchange for payments or other incentives. Demand-response resources may also be provided by intermediaries that combine the demand-response activities—for example, reductions in use of air-conditioning or household appliances at peak times—of multiple retail consumers to provide the quantity of demand-response resources required to participate in wholesale markets. [38] These intermediaries may include retail service providers or utilities that have made arrangements with their customers through retail demand-response programs they administer to reduce demand in exchange for compensation or lower prices. It may also include third– party entities referred to as "aggregators" that perform similar functions by combining the demand-response activities of independent retail consumers. In some cases, these intermediaries combine a large number of small reductions made by many consumers. In other cases, they seek out medium and larger businesses to identify profitable opportunities to reduce larger amounts of demand when needed. Collectively, we refer to these entities as "demand-response providers".

In addition, demand-response resources can be used in wholesale markets to provide a wide range of services. Specifically, individual RTOs have allowed demand-response resources to be used to provide energy, capacity, and ancillary services to varying degrees. For example, according to documentation from PJM Interconnection,[39] demand-response resources are used to provide each of the three services within PJM Interconnection. Specifically, these services are as follows:

- **Energy.** Demand-response activities can help ensure that the generation and consumption of electricity remain in balance, with demand-response resources providing an alternative to energy scheduled from power plants. In RTO markets, demand-response providers can place offers to provide specified amounts of electricity during specific hours at specific prices. They provide this electricity by reducing their or their customers' demand from levels they had expected to consume. Unlike the generators that are also bidding in these markets, which produce additional electricity by increasing the electricity generation of a power plant, demand-response providers make electricity available to the market by not consuming it. Demand-response resources may be scheduled if they are among the least costly options for addressing energy needs at a particular location.

- **Capacity.** Demand-response resources can act as an alternative to power plant operators agreeing to be available to generate electricity at a future time. Demand-response providers agree to reduce their own or their customers' electricity consumption at a future time when the grid operator determines such actions are needed.
- **Ancillary services.** Demand-response resources can act as an alternative to using changes in the amount of electricity generated to stabilize the grid. Grid operators may use demand-response resources for a short period of time to help stabilize the grid and ensure that electricity generated matches demand on a moment-tomoment basis.

FERC Has Taken Recent Steps to Make Demand-Response Rules More Consistent

Beginning in 2008, FERC issued a series of regulatory orders that establish more consistent rules related to demand-response activities for all RTOs. As shown in table 1, these orders establish a more standardized framework of rules for, among other things, how RTOs quantify and compensate demand-response activities in the markets they administer.

These orders have addressed several aspects of demand-response activities. For example, in Order 676-G, FERC adopted standards established by the North American Energy Standards Board that provide detailed guidance about quantifying consumers' demand-response activities.[40] Quantifying demand-response activities requires creating baselines—administrative estimates of consumers' expected electricity consumption for every hour of every day of the year against which any reductions in electricity use from demand-response activities are measured. Because consumer electricity use typically varies throughout the day, RTOs have no way of knowing exactly how much electricity a consumer is planning to use at specific times. The baseline—that is, the estimated amount of electricity a consumer would have used if not participating in demand-response activities—is key to determining the amount of electricity reduction for which a demand-response provider will be compensated. Additionally, through Order 745, FERC established a framework for determining the level of compensation for consumers' demand-response activities. The order generally requires that, when certain conditions are met, demand-response providers receive the market price for electricity, equal to what owners of power plants would be paid.

Table 1. Three Key FERC Orders Related to Demand-Response Activities

FERC order	Date	Description of key actions
Order 719	2008	• Requires Regional Transmission Organizations (RTO) to accept bids for demand-response resources in their markets for certain ancillary services, among other things • Permits entities called aggregators that combine the demand-response activities of multiple retail consumers into RTO markets, assuming such activity is not precluded by state law
Order 745[a]	2011	• Requires RTOs to pay providers of demand-response (including consumers) in wholesale energy markets the market price for electricity if doing so: (1) displaces electricity generation in a way that helps an RTO balance supply and demand and (2) is deemed cost-effective, meaning that the benefit from the reduction of the market price resulting from demand-response activities is greater than any money paid for the demand-response activities
Order 676-G	2013	• Incorporated by reference certain standards related to quantifying demand-response activities—including specific processes to help with measurement and verification of demand-response activities and common definitions and processes regarding demand-response activities in organizedwholesale electric markets

Sources: GAO analysis of FERC orders and other filings.

[a]Order 745 is currently being contested in the U.S. Court of Appeals for the D.C. Circuit.

FERC Collects Data and Reports on Demand-Response Activities, but These Efforts Have Limitations

Since 2006, FERC has taken steps to collect data and report on demand-response activities, but these efforts have limitations. In particular, electricity markets have changed substantially since FERC began undertaking these efforts, but FERC has not reviewed the scope of its data collection and reporting efforts to determine whether additional data should be included. Further, FERC has, in some limited instances, made certain adjustments after these data are collected and before making them available to the public but does not fully document these adjustments or the reasons for making them.

FERC Has Taken Steps to Collect and Report Data on Demand-Response Activities

In accordance with the Energy Policy Act of 2005, FERC has collected data used to develop annual reports—FERC's *Assessment of Demand Response and Advanced Metering*—about the extent to which advanced meters are used and consumers' demand-response activities in the United States.[41] To support the development of these annual reports, FERC has conducted a nationwide, voluntary survey every other year to collect information from utilities and other entities, such as RTOs, on their use of advanced meters, consumer participation in demand-response programs, and the extent to which consumers' demand-response activities reduce peak demand. FERC makes the original survey data available on its website and summarizes key statistics about demand-response activities and advanced metering based on this survey and other sources in its annual report.[42] For example, FERC's 2012 report included statistics on the potential reduction in peak demand from consumers' participation in demand-response activities in total, by program approach (e.g., specific time-based pricing approaches),[43] by market (e.g., wholesale and retail), and, for retail demand-response activities, by class (e.g., commercial, industrial, and residential). The FERC survey data and report are the only source of broad data on demand-response activities we identified with this much detailed information by program approach. According to FERC officials, they are not aware of any other comprehensive data sources with data on demand-response activities and consumer participation by program approach.

Other sources of data on demand-response activities, while useful, are more limited in scope. For example, RTOs collect some data, but they focus only on a specific RTO region, and the RTOs may not collect consistent information for purposes of comparison across RTOs. The EIA also collects some data on demand-response activities; however, these data only focus on retail markets. Additionally, the North American Electric Reliability

Corporation, known as NERC, collects some data but has only performed mandatory data collections since 2011. These data primarily focus on operator-initiated approaches, although a 2011 report from NERC states that there are plans to expand reporting to include additional consumer-initiated approaches in the future.

FERC Has Not Reviewed the Scope of Its Data Collection and Reporting

Since it initially designed its survey 8 years ago, FERC has considered some potential improvements to the survey, but it has not comprehensively reviewed the scope of its data collection and reporting efforts to address certain data limitations and changes in electricity markets over this period. FERC officials told us that, when designing the initial 2006 survey and annual report format, FERC sought to collect and report data that were consistent with the statutory requirements outlined in the Energy Policy Act while minimizing respondent burden to improve the response rate for its voluntary survey. The Energy Policy Act requires FERC to report on existing demand-response approaches, the annual size of demand resources, and regulatory barriers to improving consumer participation in demand-response activities and peak reduction programs, among other things. FERC's report generally addresses these issues but, in some cases, the information it provides is limited and does not include some additional information or details that may be useful to data users— such as regulators, utilities, and the public—for further documenting changes in trends in demand-response activities and progress in addressing certain barriers. Examples are as follows:

- FERC collects and reports data on the extent to which demand-response activities at utilities and other entities surveyed reduce peak demand in megawatts (MW), but it does not collect or report data on what the total peak demand is for these reporting utilities and other entities. Without these data, the potential reduction in peak demand that reporting utilities' and other entities' demand-response activities achieve cannot be calculated as a percentage of their total peak demand, potentially limiting users' ability to understand the impact of consumers' demand-response activities.
- FERC reported in its 2012 report that the limited number of retail consumers paying prices that vary with the cost of serving them is an

ongoing barrier to expanding demand-response activities, but its report provides limited data on consumer participation in approaches, such as real-time pricing programs, that could potentially address this barrier. Specifically, the report provides information on the number of utilities and other entities offering certain programs with prices that vary with the cost of serving consumers, such as time-of-use prices and real-time prices. However, the report does not provide much information on the number of consumers participating in these approaches over time—information needed to understand trends in the use of these approaches and whether steps are needed to encourage additional consumer participation.[44]

- FERC does not collect some potentially valuable data about the characteristics of consumers providing demand–response resources. For example, FERC officials told us they do not collect data about the class of consumers —e.g., residential, commercial, and industrial—providing demand-response resources in the RTO markets they regulate, although FERC does collect this information about consumers participating in retail programs. In addition, FERC does not collect data on the size of consumers—for example, small businesses compared with large industrial manufacturers—participating in demand-response activities. Not having these data limits data users' understanding of the extent to which different types of consumers are participating in demand-response activities and whether additional opportunities exist for increasing the participation of certain types of consumers. Based on estimates the individual RTOs provided, demand-response resources are typically provided by larger consumers, such as industrial and commercial facilities. Each RTO collects data about consumers in different categories and groups the data in different ways. For example, data collected by one RTO—New York ISO—indicate that approximately 57 percent of the demand-response resources in its region are from the industrial sector and 14 percent are from the commercial sector.[45] Other RTOs told us that no data were available on the categories of customers providing demand-response resources. Another RTO—ISO New England—told us that all the demand-response resources in its region are provided by industrial and commercial consumers, but that disaggregated data are not available.[46]

Moreover, FERC officials agreed that there have been significant changes in the electricity markets and participation in demand-response activities since the survey was initially developed. FERC staff considered some potential improvements to the survey instrument, including ways to make questions less burdensome and improve data quality. However, these officials told us that FERC did not comprehensively review the content of the survey or its final report, instead seeking to make its reporting consistent across years. FERC officials also noted that changes to its survey will need to be approved by the Office of Management and Budget.[47]

We have previously reported that evaluation can play a key role in program management and oversight—including evaluation of activities with an identifiable purpose.[48] In this context, FERC's data collection and reporting efforts to comply with the Energy Policy Act of 2005 would benefit from such an evaluation in light of the changes FERC acknowledges have occurred in electricity markets and in demand-response activities more specifically. Such an evaluation can provide feedback on program design and execution, and the results may be used to improve the design of the program. In addition, the National Research Council's Committee on National Statistics has reported in its *Principles and Practices for a Federal Statistical Agency*, that statistical agencies should continually look to improve their data systems to provide information that is accurate, timely, and relevant for changing public policy and data user needs. Although FERC is not a federal statistical agency, we believe the practices outlined in this publication are relevant to its data collection and reporting efforts because FERC is uniquely positioned to collect these data, and they remain the only source of broad demand-response data we identified with detailed information about demand-response approaches. Other federal agencies that are not statistical agencies may find it useful to periodically reassess the data they collect. For example, the Merit Systems Protection Board, which is also not a federal statistical agency, has periodically reassessed the content of a key survey it produces. Specifically, the Merit Systems Protection Board has been administering its Merit Principles Survey for the past 30 years to capture the attitudes, opinions, and views of the federal workforce and has stated that it has included a core set of items in its survey repeatedly, allowing comparisons over time, but has changed the survey considerably, reflecting the need to cover timely research topics. By not reviewing the contents of its survey on demand-response activities and annual report in light of the significant changes in the electricity market and demand-response activities over the last 8 years, FERC cannot ensure that its survey and report fully capture information that is most useful to data users today. As a result, information that could assist regulators in determining how to focus their oversight efforts—data on the impact of demand-response activities; the extent to which progress has been made in addressing barriers to expanding demand-response activities, such as the limited number of retail consumers paying prices that vary with the cost of serving them; and trends in consumer participation—may not be readily available. Without additional evaluation of its program activity responsible for its annual *Assessment of Demand Response and Advanced Metering*—the only data collection we identified with this level of detailed information—FERC may be missing opportunities to improve the report and survey's design, which could limit users' ability to understand the impact of demand-response activities and determine whether changes are needed to improve the effectiveness of demand-response efforts.

FERC Does Not Fully Document Adjustments It Makes to Its Data

FERC adjusts some survey data collected for its annual *Assessment of Demand Response and Advanced Metering* report before publishing them; however, these adjustments are not well documented. The original data FERC collects from its survey are available to the public on its website, but these data do not always match data in FERC's reports. FERC officials told us that, in some limited cases, they used their judgment to adjust the original survey data to improve their quality and accuracy prior to using these data in the reports FERC issues to the public. For example, FERC staff told us that they have previously modified the survey data to ensure duplicate data on demand-response activities are not reported in both the retail and wholesale market categories and to improve the consistency of the data. However, FERC neither fully documents these adjustments, or the reasons for them internally or in its annual reports, nor makes its final, modified data set available to the public. As a result, it is difficult for data users to replicate the statistics in FERC's annual reports, which could limit the usefulness of the data to these users. We compared key statistics included in FERC's 2012 report and the associated original survey data reported on FERC's website and were unable to replicate FERC's results in some cases. For example, in some cases, our analysis of the original survey data yielded different results about the extent to which certain demand-response approaches are used at the wholesale level than what FERC published in its annual report. Best practices for data management advise that key steps to modify data be documented. Specifically, the Office of Management and Budget's 2006 *Standards and Guidelines for Statistical Surveys* advises that data collected through surveys should be coded to indicate any actions taken during editing or that copies of the unedited data, along with the edited data, be retained. Because FERC neither fully documents the modifications it makes to the data or maintains a final version of the modified data, FERC officials could not provide reasons for many of the specific differences we identified between the original survey data and the data reported in FERC's 2012 annual report or verify whether these differences were the result of appropriate modifications or errors. These officials told us they had not identified a need to document this information to date, but that they would consider documenting it in the future. Although the rationale for FERC's data modifications may be sound, because they are not fully documented, it is unclear what changes were made, the reasons they were made, and whether these changes are appropriate. Furthermore, since the users of these data, such as state regulators and the public, may not have the means or ability to easily replicate FERC's efforts to modify the survey data, they must either analyze the original survey data or rely on only the statistics that FERC included in its final report—options which may be less informative. This could, for example, limit data users' understanding of how the number of consumers participating in certain demand-response approaches has changed over time—information that could be useful to regulators for understanding the extent to which consumer willingness to participate in certain approaches is, or is not, changing. By not fully documenting the adjustments made to its data, FERC is limiting the usefulness of these data to users and limiting their transparency for analysis. Greater transparency of these data could provide a better foundation for analysis of trends in specific demand-response approaches and the extent to which progress has been made in addressing barriers to demand-response activities.

Demand-Response Activities Have Increased Overall, but Their Characteristics Have Varied

The extent of demand-response activities has increased overall since our 2004 report, more than doubling between 2005 and 2011. Specifically, according to data reported in FERC's 2012 *Assessment of Demand Response and Advanced Metering* report, the extent of demand-response activities reported by utilities and other entities responding to FERC's survey more than doubled from a total of 29,653 MW of potential reduction in peak demand in 2005 to 66,351 MW in 2011,[49] or about 8.5 percent of the peak U.S. demand in 2011.[50] Of this 66,351 MW, 57 percent (37,543 MW) was provided through retail demand-response activities, while 43 percent (28,807 MW) was provided through wholesale demand-response activities.[51] Demand–response activities in both retail and wholesale markets have increased over this same period, but their characteristics have varied. In retail markets, FERC data indicate that the quantity of demand-response activities increased 81 percent from 2005 through 2011. Further, operator-initiated approaches were more widely used than consumer-initiated approaches. In wholesale markets, FERC data indicate that demand-response activities more than tripled from 2005 through 2011, but the extent of demand-response activities has varied by RTO region over time and by the services provided.

Demand-Response Activities in Retail Markets Have Increased Overall, but Consumer Type and Approaches Varied

FERC data indicate that the extent of demand-response activities in retail markets has increased overall but varied by consumer type and approach. Specifically, data from FERC's 2012 *Assessment of Demand Response and Advanced Metering* report indicate that the extent of retail demand-response activities has increased 81 percent overall from a reported 20,754 MW of potential reduction in peak demand in 2005 to a reported 37,543 MW in 2011. Commercial and industrial consumers were responsible for more of these retail demand-response activities than residential consumers. For example, of the 37,543 MW of potential reduction in peak demand from retail demand-response activities in 2011, 28,088 MW (75 percent) was from commercial and industrial consumers, while 8,134 MW was from residential consumers (22 percent).[52] The relatively lower contribution in MW of demand-response activities by residential consumers is particularly notable because, according to a 2009 FERC report, residential consumers represent the most untapped potential for demand-response activities.[53] Demand-response activities from residential consumers can be particularly important because residential consumers can be responsible for a large share of peak demand, which can strongly affect prices during the hours of peak electricity consumption. For example, according to data from the Texas grid operator, over 50 percent of peak demand during Texas summers may come from residential consumers.

Table 2. Examples of Operator-Initiated Approaches

Name	Description	Number of consumers enrolled in this approach (as a percentage of consumers enrolled in operator-initiated approaches)	Potential reduction in peakdemand (as a percentage ofpotential reduction in peakdemand from all operator-initiatedapproaches)
Direct demand control	Compensates consumers for allowing the utility or grid operator to remotely interrupt electricity use by one or more electrical devices, such as pool pumps or air conditioners. In some cases, electricity may be interrupted for an hour or more; in other cases, the operator may "cycle" the equipment—that is, shut it down for several short periods, which can have less impact on the consumer.	5.8 million (97 percent)	9,112 MW (33 percent)
Interruptible prices	Participants—typically, large industrial or commercial consumers—receive a discount on electricity prices paid in exchange for agreeing to interrupt electricity use when directed to do so by the grid operator. In some cases, consumers give grid operators the ability to interrupt their electricity use directly by a preestablished amount for a certain number of hours per year.	.04 million (about 1 percent)	14,960 MW (55 percent)

Sources: GAO analysis of 2011 FERC survey data collected for FERC's 2012 *Assessment of Demand Response and Advanced Metering* and other sources.

Data from FERC and EIA also indicate that retail consumer participation in demand-response programs varies by approach, with operator-initiated approaches more widely used than consumer-initiated approaches.[54]

Data collected for FERC's 2012 report indicate that approximately 6.5 percent of retail consumers of utilities and other entities responding to the survey—about 8.5 million of 130.6 million consumers—were enrolled in a demand-response program in 2011.[55] Of these 8.5 million consumers, approximately 6.0 million (71 percent) participated in programs that used operator-initiated approaches.[56] Consumers enrolled in demand-response programs using operator-initiated approaches accounted for approximately 27,422 MW of potential reduction in peak demand for 2011. Industrial and commercial retail consumers provided 19,089 MW (70 percent) of this potential reduction, and residential consumers provided 7,151 MW (26 percent).[57] Table 2 shows the extent to which consumers participate in two key operator-initiated approaches.

Of the 8.5 million consumers who utilities and other entities reported as participating in demand-response programs, approximately 2.3 million (27 percent) participated in programs that used consumer-initiated approaches, including some retail pricing plans that sought to better align consumer prices with the cost of serving those consumers.[58] According to our analysis of FERC's survey data for 2011, consumers enrolled in demand-response programs that used these approaches accounted for approximately 9,920 MW of potential reduction in peak demand for the given year. Industrial and commercial retail consumers provided 8,893 MW (90 percent) of this 9,920 MW of the potential reduction. Table 3 shows the extent to which consumers participate in three key types of consumer-initiated approaches.

In addition to FERC's 2011 survey data, data from an EIA survey of utilities in 2011 also indicate that more consumers reported participating in programs that use operator-initiated approaches than consumer-initiated approaches.[59] According to the EIA data, 3.7 percent of retail consumers (5.4 million of 144.5 million) of utilities that responded to the survey reported participating in operator-initiated approaches in 2011, and 2.8 percent of retail consumers (4.0 million of 144.5 million) of such utilities reported participating in consumer-initiated approaches. EIA data show that reported retail demand-response activities resulted in the potential to reduce peak electricity demand by 26,596 MW in 2011. Actual reductions in peak electricity demand—a result of consumers' actual demand-response activities—in 2011 were much lower—12,126 MW.

Table 3. Examples of Consumer-Initiated Approaches

Name	Description	Number of consumers enrolled in this approach (as a percentage of consumers enrolled in consumer-initiated approaches)	Potential reduction inpeak demand (as apercentage of potentialreduction in peakdemand from allconsumer-initiatedapproaches)
Time-of-use prices	Sets preestablished prices for predetermined parts of the day (i.e., off-peak, often during the night and early morning; midpeak, often during the day and late evening; peak, often in the late afternoon and early evening). The highest prices are established for peak periods when demand and the cost of serving consumers are generally highest, based on historical and projected cost and consumption information. Periods may vary seasonally, for example, with different peak periods in the summer than in the winter. Prices generally remain consistent throughout a given period, regardless of specific levels of hourly demand or changes in the cost of serving consumers.	2.2 million (98 percent)	7,373 MW (74 percent)
Critical peak prices[a]	In some cases, in addition to the time-of-use prices, a utility may also establish a “critical peak price,” which is higher than the on-peak price and is designed to encourage consumers to make even more significant reductions in their	0.02 million (about 1 percent)	431 MW (4 percent)

Name	Description	Number of consumers enrolled in this approach (as a percentage of consumers enrolled in consumer-initiated approaches)	Potential reduction inpeak demand (as apercentage of potentialreduction in peakdemand from allconsumer-initiatedapproaches)
	electricity use during a few specific hours. Such a price would be initiated in response to particularly high costs of serving consumers or reliability concerns. A critical peak price is generally used only for a limited number of days and hours as determined by the utility, and consumers may not know that a critical peak price will go into effect until the day before or day of.		
Real-time prices	Consumers are charged prices that typically vary at least hourly based on their utility or retail service providers' cost of serving them. For example, this may include prices that vary with the wholesale price of electricity.	0.02 million (about 1 percent)	1,905 MW (19 percent)

Sources: GAO analysis of 2011 FERC survey data collected for FERC's 2012 *Assessment of Demand Response and Advanced Metering* and other sources.

[a]This included what FERC called "critical peak pricing" and "critical peak pricing with load control" in its 2012 report.

Wholesale Demand-Response Activities Have Increased Overall and Have Varied by Region and the Service Provided

Data from FERC and the RTOs indicate that the extent of wholesale demand-response activities has increased overall but varies regionally and by the service provided. In its 2012 *Assessment of Demand Response and*

Advanced Metering report, FERC reported data that show that the extent of wholesale demand-response activities has increased overall, more than tripling from a reported 8,899 MW of potential reduction in peak demand in 2005 to 28,807 MW of potential reduction in peak demand in 2011. According to RTO data, these demand-response resources in wholesale markets overseen by each RTO have varied over time, as shown in figure 3.

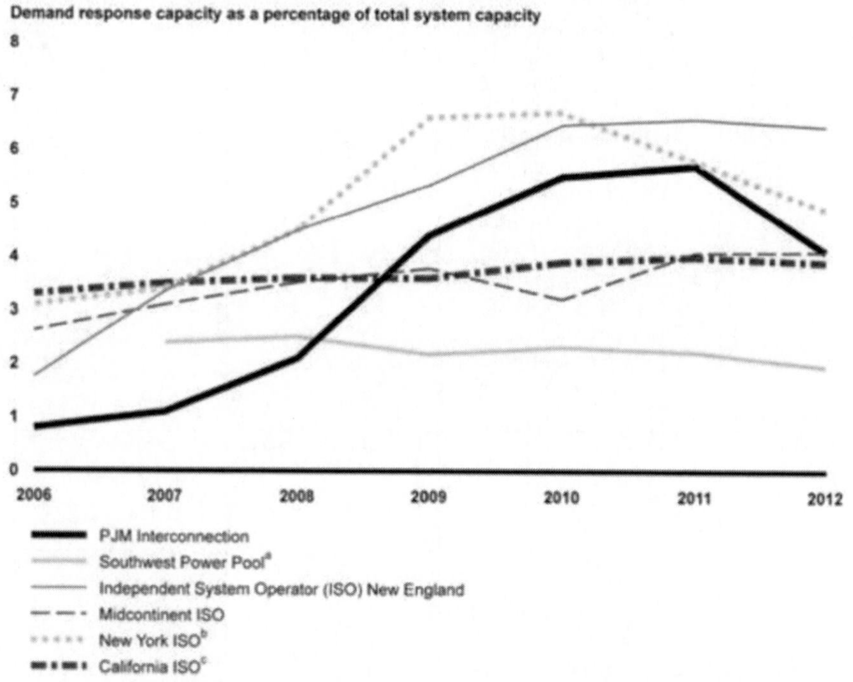

Source: Data provided by the above Regional Transmission Organizations (RTO).

Note: This figure shows the percentage of each RTO's demand-response capacity as a percentage of each RTO system's total capacity to meet consumer demand (i.e., "total installed capacity"). These numbers were initially prepared by the RTOs for FERC as a part of two annual reports on RTO performance metrics. The RTOs provided data for more recent years to us. Given the unique nature of each RTO region, including the markets RTOs offer and opportunities for demand-response activities, each RTO's methodology for calculating this metric may vary. Because most Electric Reliability Council of Texas activities are not regulated by FERC, the Electric Reliability Council of Texas was not required to submit information to FERC for this performance metric.

[a]The Southwest Power Pool provided updated data to us for this metric. As a result, its data do not match the data reported in the FERC annual reports on RTO

performance metrics. Additionally, because the Southwest Power Pool's markets were not active in 2006, data are not available for that year.

[b]Beginning with the 2010 data, New York ISO made modifications to its approach for calculating this metric.

[c]As initially reported to FERC, the California Independent System Operator included retail demand-response activities and interruptible load programs in its calculation of regional demand-response activities. With one exception, these retail programs are not operated or triggered by the California ISO.

Figure 3. Regional Transmission Organization Demand-Response Capacity as a Percentage of Total System Capacity (2006 – 2012).

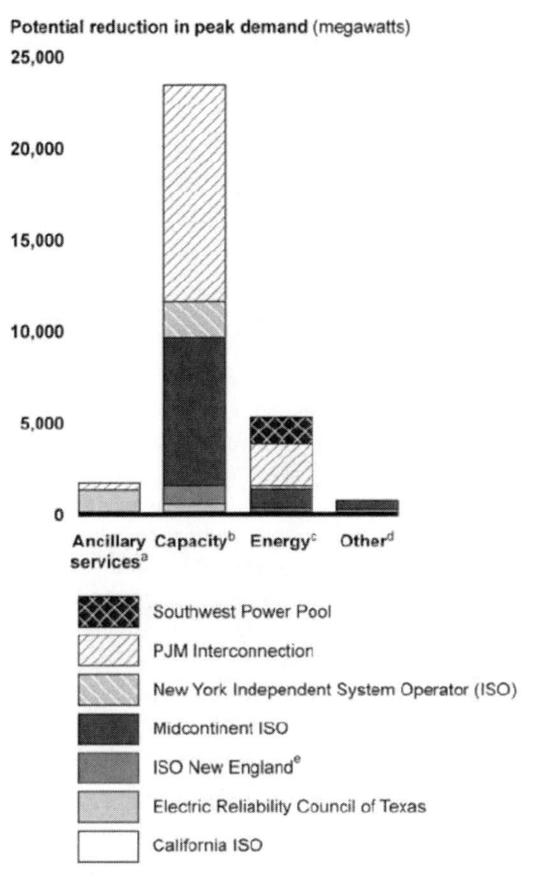

Source: GAO analysis of data from the Federal Energy Regulatory Commission and the above Regional Transmission Organizations (RTO).

Note: This figure provides data on the potential reduction in peak demand from demand-response resources in RTO areas. These demand-response resources are reflected in both the retail and wholesale demand-response activity totals presented in other parts of this report. The RTOs provided these data to the Federal Energy Regulatory Commission (FERC) in the survey associated with FERC's 2012 *Assessment of Demand Response and Advanced Metering* report. With assistance from the RTOs, we categorized RTO demand-response programs based on whether they addressed a need for ancillary services, capacity, energy, or other. In some cases, demand-response programs have been updated or changed by the RTOs since this information was reported to FERC. Additionally, FERC took various steps to modify reported categories for the purpose of improving data quality prior to reporting similar information in its 2012 *Assessment of Demand Response and Advanced Metering* report. Because these modifications were not documented, we were unable to verify their appropriateness for inclusion in this analysis. As such, in all cases but one, we used the original survey data reported on FERC's website for this analysis. In the case of data from the Midcontinent Independent System Operator, FERC staff informed us that the data reported on the agency website was not correct and provided us with the corrected survey data.

[a]Ancillary services involve demand-response providers making small adjustments in the amount of electricity used or delivered for short periods of time to help stabilize the grid.

[b]Capacity involves demand-response providers making commitments to the RTO to reduce their or their customers' use of electricity when the grid operator directs them to. In some cases when requested by the grid operator, for example, due to a concern about reliability, these commitments may result in demand-response activities for energy, which are not reflected in this graphic.

[c]Energy involves demand-response providers lowering their or their customers' use of electricity, which can help maintain the overall balance of electricity generation and consumption.

[d]The other category includes demand-response resources from Midcontinent Independent System Operator and California Independent System Operator that are used to provide both energy or ancillary services. To avoid double counting, we included these demand-response activities in the other category.

[e]For ISO New England, we excluded 877 MW of potential reduction in peak demand reported to FERC because ISO New England explained that this is more properly categorized as energy efficiency, rather than demand-response activities.

Figure 4. Demand-Response Resources in Regional Transmission Organization Regions in 2011 Used to Provide Ancillary Services, Capacity, and Energy, Measured in Megawatts of Reported Potential Reduction in Peak Demand.

The extent of wholesale demand-response activities in RTOs also varies by the service they provide, with demand-response resources used to provide capacity being the most common. Demand-response resources that provide capacity involve demand-response providers making commitments to the RTO to reduce their or their customers' use of electricity when the grid operator directs them to do so, for example, because of reliability concerns from higher than expected demand or a generating unit that was expected to produce electricity but could not do so. According to stakeholders, these commitments to reduce demand are functionally similar to power plant operators agreeing to increase their generation of electricity. As shown in figure 4, data from FERC and the RTOs indicate that 76 percent of the wholesale demand-response resources in the RTO regions were used to provide capacity.[60] Less common are demand-response resources to provide ancillary services, which, according to our analysis of FERC data, accounted for 5 percent of the demand-response resources in RTO markets in 2011. Likewise, demand-response resources to provide energy accounted for about 17 percent of demand-response resources in RTO markets, according to our analysis of FERC's data.

Demand-Response Efforts Have Resulted in Benefits, but Current Efforts Continue to Pose Challenges in Wholesale Markets

According to stakeholders, current demand-response efforts provide benefits for consumers, including increasing reliability, lower prices, and delaying the need to develop new power plants and transmission lines. However, FERC's efforts to remove barriers and to encourage demand-response activities have made wholesale markets more complex by introducing administrative functions that, according to stakeholders, have led to challenges, and it is too soon to tell whether FERC's steps to address these challenges will be effective. In addition, according to some stakeholders and reports we reviewed, retail prices remain largely unresponsive to market conditions, which poses challenges by limiting the potential for consumers to respond to changes in the cost of producing electricity or prices in wholesale markets.

Stakeholders Identified Examples of Benefits Provided by Demand-Response Efforts

Stakeholders we interviewed identified examples of how demand-response efforts have resulted in benefits, including increased reliability, lower prices, and delayed need to develop additional power plants and transmission lines. Specifically, examples are as follows:

- **Increased reliability**. Many stakeholders noted that demand-response activities can enhance the reliability of the electricity system by providing an additional tool to manage emergencies, such as electricity shortages. For example, according to documentation from PJM Interconnection, the demand-response activities of consumers in its region helped the RTO maintain reliability in 2013 during an unusual September heat wave that led to two of the highest electricity use days of the year since July. According to this documentation, demand-response activities estimated to total 5,949 MW—comparable to the electricity output of five nuclear power plants—helped stabilize the grid. In addition, in January 2014, cold temperatures and power plant outages in Texas triggered an emergency reliability alert. ERCOT—Texas' grid operator—utilized the demand-response activities of consumers in the region, in addition to voluntary requests for consumers to conserve activity, to help stabilize the grid.
- **Lower prices**. Several stakeholders noted that demand-response activities lower wholesale market prices by helping grid operators avert the need to use the most costly power plants during periods of otherwise high electricity demand. For example, according to representatives from PJM Interconnection, prices spiked on July 17, 2012, during a heat wave, when electricity demand rose to its highest levels that year. According to these representatives, demand-response activities served as an alternative to generating additional electricity, which lowered prices, although given the complex set of factors like weather and location that affect prices, the representatives could not quantify the extent of the price reduction attributable to demand-response activities.
- **Delayed need for power plants and transmission lines**. Several stakeholders we spoke with—including representatives from PJM Interconnection; Midcontinent Independent System Operator;[61] and

ISO New England—noted that demand-response activities may help delay the need to develop additional power plants and transmission lines. For example, according to documents from the Midcontinent Independent System Operator, demand-response activities in its region delayed the need to construct new power plants, which amounted to an estimated annual benefit of between $112 and $146 million.

FERC's Efforts to Remove Barriers and Encourage Demand-Response Activities Have Made Wholesale Markets More Complex and Introduced Challenges, and It Is Too Soon to Evaluate Steps to Address Challenges

FERC's efforts to remove barriers and to encourage demand-response activities in wholesale markets have added complexity to these markets by introducing administrative functions that, according to stakeholders, have led to challenges. Stakeholders identified key challenges to quantifying and compensating wholesale demand-response activities, and it is too soon to evaluate whether FERC's steps to address these challenges will be effective.

Stakeholders Stated That Quantifying Wholesale Demand-Response Activities Poses Two Key Challenges That Require Time and Resources to Address

Stakeholders we spoke with highlighted two key challenges to quantifying demand-response activities: (1) developing baselines and (2) the potential for manipulation of baselines. FERC has taken steps to address these challenges by adopting standards for quantifying demand-response activities and undertaking enforcement activities, but these steps require time and resources, and it is too soon to tell whether they will be effective.

First, several stakeholders said that developing baselines in electricity markets—that is, an estimate of how much electricity a consumer would have consumed if not for their demand-response activities—can be difficult. Individual electricity consumption reflects factors unique to individual consumers that are inherently difficult to predict. Specifically, consumers' past electricity use does not necessarily predict future use because electricity use depends on many variables, such as weather and, for large industrial consumers, production cycles. For example, the electricity demand of some industrial and commercial consumers is difficult to estimate because their electricity consumption varies based on changes in the demand for the products they produce. Further, determining when to measure a baseline can be difficult since consumers' electricity use may vary frequently and electricity use before and after a consumer's demand-response activities may not accurately reflect the extent of the consumer's demand-response contribution. For example, comments from an industrial coalition and two demand-response aggregators to FERC describe a potential situation in which a steelmaker has a furnace temporarily out of service for maintenance. After maintenance is completed, if the steelmaker chooses to take a demand-response action by delaying its next production cycle, measuring this steelmaker's baseline immediately before the steelmaker took the demand-response action—when its furnace was out of service—would not reflect the steelmaker's contribution. Baselines can have significant implications for demand-response activities. If a baseline is set too high, consumers may be compensated for a greater quantity of electricity resulting from their demand-response actions than the quantity they actually provided, potentially raising costs to all electricity consumers who ultimately pay for demand-response activities. If the baseline is set too low, consumers may not be credited with providing the quantity of electricity resulting from the demand-response actions they actually provided, and they may be less willing to take demand-response actions in the future, limiting the potential benefits. As a result, RTOs and demand-response providers must devote resources to the efforts of developing reasonable and fair baselines for demand-response programs to operate effectively.

Second, some stakeholders noted that using baselines as a key component of compensation for demand-response activities subjects them to manipulation, which requires RTOs and FERC to devote time and resources to oversight and enforcement. For example, in recent years, FERC has identified multiple instances in which consumers manipulated their baseline to receive additional financial compensation for demand-response activities or to avoid financial penalties for not providing the quantity of demand-response activities they agreed to. Specifically, in June 2013, FERC reported what it believed were irregular activities by a company that manages sports and entertainment facilities. According to a FERC document, witnesses reported that stadium lighting at one of the company's baseball stadiums was turned on 2 hours before a demand-response event was scheduled to begin.[62] No games were scheduled for that day, indicating that the increased electricity use was not needed for operations at the ballpark. These actions could have artificially inflated the company's baseline, thereby increasing the company's compensation for the reduction in demand that resulted from switching the lights off during the demand-response event. FERC recently approved a $1.3 million settlement with the company.[63] More recently, FERC fined two Maine paper mills after concluding that they had manipulated New England's demand-response programs.[64] In both cases, FERC determined that the paper mills had improperly set their baseline electricity usage by lowering their use of on-site generation below what was their normal practice. According to FERC, doing so increased their consumption of electricity from the grid and inflated their baselines. Once the baseline was set, FERC determined that the mills returned to their normal practice of using their on-site generation, which made it appear that they had taken demand-response actions by lowering their use of electricity from the grid. FERC recently approved an approximately $3 million settlement with one paper mill, and the other case is currently being contested in court. FERC officials told us that FERC's enforcement office continues to pursue investigations related to fraudulent demand-response activities. As a result of the potential for such manipulations, RTOs and FERC must devote time and resources toward oversight and enforcement tasks, such as monitoring, investigating, and adjudicating potential violations of the rules for demand-response activities.

Stakeholders Stated That Compensating Wholesale Demand-Response Activities Also Poses Challenges and Disagreed about FERC's Approach

Stakeholders we spoke with also highlighted challenges to compensating demand-response activities. The stakeholders we spoke with disagreed on the value of demand-response activities relative to electricity generation and how to compensate consumers for their demand-response activities. FERC sought to address these challenges in Order 745, issued in 2011, which provides rules for compensating consumers in wholesale energy markets, but it is too soon to tell if this will be effective.[65]

Some stakeholders noted that reasonable compensation for demand-response activities is needed to ensure an appropriate amount of participation. If the quantity of electricity reduced as a result of demand-response activities is too small, the price and reliability benefits that demand-response activities provide may be reduced. In contrast, if the quantity of electricity reduced as a result of demand-response activities is too high, it may dampen the incentives to invest in new power plants, which could reduce their availability for meeting demand in the long run.

Central to the issue of reasonable compensation is the fact that, because both demand-response activities and electricity generation from power plants can be used to help meet demand for electricity, they compete for compensation in the wholesale market.

Some stakeholders told us that they believe that demand-response providers should receive less compensation than power plants for the services they provide. Specifically, these stakeholders said the following:

- Some stakeholders noted that power plants—assets with long useful lives—are more dependable in the long run than demand-response resources. For example, these stakeholders told us that owners of power plants are typically obligated to ensure that power plants are available to generate electricity. In contrast, these stakeholders noted that there may not be such a requirement for mandatory participation by demand-response providers. For example, representatives from one RTO noted that consumers enter into agreements to provide demand-response resources through aggregators and may change their availability on a month-to-month basis. As a result, they said that the RTO is not able to accurately predict how many demand-response resources its region will have in the future. In addition, while the amount of electricity generation that power plants can generally provide is known, there may be limits to how often consumers can be requested to curtail their electricity consumption and for how long. For example, the market rules for PJM Interconnection's most widely subscribed demand-response program limit PJM's requests of customers for demand-response activities to no more than 10 interruptions from June through September with a maximum interruption of 6 hours. Representatives from PJM Interconnection told us they are attempting to increase the use of demand-response approaches with fewer restrictions.[66]
- Several stakeholders noted that providing equal compensation for demand-response activities as electricity generation may result in benefits to demand-response providers in excess of what would be economically justified. Several stated that, in their view, if these

resources are compensated equally, the providers are effectively benefitting twice—once when they are paid for their demand-response activities and a second time because they save money by not having to purchase as much electricity as they were originally planning to. One stakeholder noted that while it may be reasonable to provide compensation to demand-response providers at a level equal to power plants if the providers had first purchased the electricity and were just reselling it, demand-response providers may have not done so. In essence, demand-response providers may be compensated for agreeing to reduce their use of electricity that they may not have purchased in the first place. Some stakeholders noted that providing equal compensation could result in more demand-response resources than are economically justified.

Some stakeholders told us they believe that demand-response providers should receive compensation equal to the compensation power plants receive for generating electricity. Specifically, stakeholders said the following:

- Some stakeholders noted that providing equal compensation can encourage demand-response resources to participate in wholesale markets in which they provide benefits. According to one stakeholder, demand-response activities can provide reliability benefits, including addressing localized reliability concerns. Localized reliability concerns sometimes arise when the transmission lines leading to a local area do not have the capability to transport sufficient electricity for that area. Even though adequate electricity is available to meet overall demand, there may not be sufficient transmission available to deliver the electricity at certain points during the day or year. One stakeholder told us that, in these instances, the demand-response activities of consumers living in the local area could help resolve the reliability concern. Two other stakeholders—a representative of a demand-response aggregator and a state public utility commission official— told us that, without equal compensation, the quantity of demand-response activities in the wholesale energy markets would likely be smaller.
- Some stakeholders told us that, although demand-response activities and electricity generation are different kinds of resources, providing equal compensation is appropriate since demand-response activities provide a benefit to the market by replacing the need to have power

plants provide additional electricity. One stakeholder said that equal compensation always provides an economic benefit to consumers since FERC requires demand-response activities to be cost-effective. This means that the estimated benefit from the reduction of the wholesale market price attributable to demand-response activities should be greater than the amount of compensation paid for the demand-response activities. Another stakeholder noted that equal compensation in electricity markets is designed to provide a competitive price that balances supply and demand in the marketplace in an unbiased manner. The purpose of equal compensation is not to provide equal benefit to all resources, since each resource—including power plants with different fuel types—has varying costs and will, therefore, benefit from equal compensation to varying degrees.

In 2011, FERC issued Order 745 generally requiring that, when certain conditions are met, demand-response providers should receive equal compensation. Prior to issuance, FERC issued a Notice of Proposed Rulemaking and provided an opportunity for the public to comment. In the final order, FERC acknowledged divergent opinions on the appropriate level of compensation, but it determined that equal compensation should generally be provided for demand-response activities that provide the same services as generation. It may take time to determine whether Order 745 will have the desired effect.

Stakeholders Identified Two Additional Challenges as a Result of Demand-Response Efforts

Stakeholders identified the following two additional challenges that have developed related to demand-response efforts:

- **Environmental impacts of backup or replacement generation**.[67] Some stakeholders highlighted challenges associated with the use of backup generators for demand-response activities. Some consumers may use backup generators—on-site generating units that replace electricity that would have been provided by the grid—to generate electricity to offset some or all of their demand reductions. Although these backup generators can play an important role in maintaining reliability, they may be more polluting than the power plants serving the grid. EPA officials told us that they did not know the environmental impact of backup generation being used to offset demand-response activities and said that the impact will depend on how often backup generators are used for this purpose and their individual emissions profiles. According to an EPA final rule, starting with calendar year 2015, owners and operators of backup generators subject to EPA's rules must annually report data on the extent to which their generators are used for demand-response activities.[68]

- **Demand-response dependability**. As demand-response activities increase and become a larger percentage of overall system demand, the likelihood increases that a consumer will be called upon more often for their demand-response activities. Some stakeholders noted that consumers may become fatigued as the number of demand-response events increases, making them less likely to reduce electricity demand to agreed-upon levels. NERC has recently begun taking steps to collect data about this issue.[69]

Retail Prices Remain Unresponsive to Market Conditions, which Poses Challenges in Wholesale Markets, Including Higher Demand and Prices

Retail prices, which are outside of FERC's jurisdiction, remain largely unresponsive to wholesale market conditions, which poses challenges in wholesale markets. These unresponsive retail prices limit the potential for consumers to respond to changes in the cost of producing electricity or prices in wholesale markets which, in turn, leaves electricity consumption and wholesale prices higher than they otherwise would be. In our 2004 report,[70] we reported that a barrier to demand-response activities is that retail electricity prices generally did not vary with wholesale market conditions—such as changing demand for electricity and the cost of serving consumers—but were instead based on average electricity costs over an extended period.[71] In particular, in 2004, we concluded that retail prices that did not vary with wholesale market conditions resulted in electricity markets that do not work as well as they could, producing prices that are higher than they would be if more consumers paid varying prices. Since that time, others have also concluded that having a limited number of consumers paying prices that are responsive to market conditions may lead to higher consumer demand for electricity than would otherwise be the case. Specifically, according to a 2008 FERC report about demand-response activities, some stakeholders, and other reports we reviewed, consumers paying average, unvarying prices may use more electricity at times of the day when the cost of serving consumers is high than they would if the price they paid reflected this higher cost of serving them.[72] More recently, some stakeholders we spoke with and reports we reviewed also concluded that if consumers' electricity use is higher than it otherwise would be, electricity prices for all consumers will also be higher. Furthermore, two stakeholders and reports we reviewed noted that higher levels of consumption must be served by building additional power plants and transmission lines, which further drives up costs and ultimately retail prices paid by consumers.

FERC has also concluded that prices that are aligned with overall market conditions could provide substantial benefits. For example, in a 2009 assessment of demand-response potential, FERC estimated that forecasted peak demand in 2019 could drop by 14 percent if two types of consumer-initiated demand-response approaches—real-time prices and critical-peak prices—became the default pricing approach for consumers. [73] Consistent with this view, some stakeholders we interviewed, reports by economists, and a FERC Advance Notice of Proposed Rulemaking,[74] reported that increasing the number of consumers enrolled in consumer-initiated demand-response approaches, particularly real-time pricing programs, has the potential to lower average electricity prices for all consumers as well as provide other benefits. For example, such an approach could eliminate "cross subsidies" in which one type of consumer—consumers that currently use little electricity at high-cost times—subsidizes the behavior of other consumers—those that use larger amounts of electricity at high-cost times. In addition, such an approach could provide consumers with the incentive to make more permanent shifts in the way they consume electricity, such as by making changes to electricity consumption habits, including precooling buildings prior to peak hours rather than cooling continuously throughout the day. We also previously reported that such pricing can provide incentives for the installation of more energy efficient equipment to replace equipment that consumes large quantities of electricity during periods of high demand, such as air conditioners that run during peak periods during the summer.[75] Such pricing may also make it cost-effective for some consumers to invest in renewable energy technologies such as solar panels. The times solar power can be generated often coincide with times of peak demand, when the cost of generating electricity is higher, which may make the use of solar panels more cost-effective when consumers pay real-time prices.

In particular, FERC's data indicate that 6.5 percent of retail consumers participate in demand-response programs and approximately 2 percent in consumer-initiated approaches such as time-of-use or real-time pricing. Some stakeholders we spoke to told us that expanding the number of consumers paying prices that are responsive to market conditions—such as real-time prices—would be a more straightforward and less administratively costly alternative to FERC's demand-response efforts.

Some stakeholders highlighted the difficulties of shifting retail pricing toward prices that more closely mirror the cost of serving consumers. For example, representatives from a large industrial company told us that it is difficult to manage their operations when paying prices that vary frequently throughout the day because electricity comprises a large portion of this company's business expenses, and frequently varying prices make it difficult to plan production cycles. Two other stakeholders commented that if consumers' expected cost savings from shifting their electricity use are small, they may decide that it is not worth the effort to shift their electricity use in response to changing prices. When making this determination, consumers may consider the costs associated with managing their electricity usage in response to prices that vary frequently, including the costs of installing any needed technological infrastructure— for example, energy management control systems that allow them to automatically respond to varying prices with preprogrammed demand-response curtailment actions.

Efforts are under way in several areas to evaluate different ways of pricing electricity for retail consumers with some utilities initiating pilots. For example, Baltimore Gas and Electric completed a pilot program— converted to a permanent program in July 2013—in which residential consumers earn a bill credit for energy conserved compared with their normal usage on days identified by the utility when energy demand is high. Furthermore, Pacific Gas and Electric, which serves much of Northern and Central California, began offering a critical peak pricing program in 2008 after advanced meters had been installed. Additionally, as a part of the DOE Smart Grid Investment Grant program, DOE is helping to coordinate studies to assess consumers' responses to these new approaches.

CONCLUSION

Since our last report on demand-response activities in 2004, FERC has made efforts to remove barriers to expand the use of demand-response activities in wholesale markets, recognizing the importance of connecting consumers' decisions about electricity consumption to the wholesale markets FERC oversees. FERC has also undertaken efforts to study demand-response activities and collect data on the range of demand-response activities across the United States and report them annually, as required under the Energy Policy Act. However, the data FERC collects and reports—the only source of broad data we identified with detailed information by demand-response approach—have two key limitations. First, FERC has not reviewed the scope of its data collection and reporting efforts to determine whether they could be improved to better reflect changes in electricity markets and participation in demand-response activities. Second, in some cases, FERC makes certain adjustments after collecting these data but before using them in their reports required by Congress; however, it does not fully document these adjustments or the reasons for them. By taking steps to address these limitations, FERC could make its data more informative and transparent to data users and ensure that Congress has a better picture of demand-response activities—something it sought in the Energy Policy Act.

Improvements in its data collection and reporting process could also benefit regulators—such as FERC and state regulators—in determining how to focus their demand-response efforts.

RECOMMENDATIONS FOR EXECUTIVE ACTION

We are making recommendations to improve the quality of FERC's annual reports required by Congress on demand-response and advanced metering activities and the data collected to support these reports. In particular, we recommend that the Chairman of FERC take the following two actions:

- Review the scope of FERC's efforts to prepare and publish an annual report that assesses demand-response resources and consider whether revisions to the data it collects could better inform users and improve the effectiveness of demand-response activities.
- Take steps to ensure that FERC staff fully document any modifications made to survey data prior to public reporting, including considering making its final, modified data set available to the public.

Agency Comments and Our Evaluation

We provided a draft of this report to FERC for review and comment. In its comments, FERC did not disagree with our findings or recommendations and stated that it would take them under advisement as it considers how best to fulfill the requirements of the Energy Policy Act of 2005. We believe in the importance of fully implementing these recommendations. FERC also provided technical comments, which we incorporated, as appropriate.

Frank Rusco
Director,
Natural Resources and Environment

Appendix I: Objectives, Scope, and Methodology

This report examines efforts to expand demand-response activities in the U.S. electricity markets and provides an update on the status of demand-response activities since we previously reported on them in 2004. Specifically, this report assesses: (1) the federal government's efforts to facilitate demand-response activities; (2) Federal Energy Regulatory Commission (FERC) efforts to collect and report data on demand-response activities; (3) changes, if any, in the extent of demand-response activities in retail and wholesale markets; and (4) key benefits and challenges, if any, of current demand-response efforts.

To assess the federal government's efforts to facilitate demand-response since our 2004 report, we reviewed federal demand-response policies and interviewed officials from FERC, the Department of Energy (DOE), and the Environmental Protection Agency (EPA), key agencies involved in demand-response policy setting. These policies included FERC demand-response orders that summarize FERC's review of demand-response proposals from individual Regional Transmission Organizations (RTO), as well as FERC orders that address demand-response activities more broadly. We also spoke with FERC officials to understand their current approach to demand-response activities in wholesale markets, including decisions about how to eliminate barriers to demand-response activities in these markets. We reviewed relevant laws that outlined requirements related to demand-response efforts for FERC and others.

To assess FERC's efforts to collect and report data on demand-response activities, we reviewed FERC's approach to gathering data for its *Assessment of Demand Response and Advanced Metering* reports, which involved analyzing various aspects of the data, analyzing FERC's approach for collecting and modifying the data, and conducting interviews with FERC officials about FERC's data collection and reporting process.

To assess the changes, if any, in the extent of demand-response activities in retail and wholesale markets since 2004, we reviewed and analyzed data on demand-response activities from FERC and the Energy Information Administration (EIA), among others. Specifically, we reviewed FERC data on demand-response approaches and related reports, including FERC's 2012 *Assessment of Demand Response and Advanced Metering* report. Where appropriate, we used these data in our report to provide information on how overall levels of demand-response activities have changed over time. We also analyzed data from FERC's survey of utility demand-response activities conducted for this 2012 assessment to identify the primary demand-response approaches in use at the retail level. FERC conducted a voluntary survey of utilities to gather data on their demand-response activities and their use of advanced meters. The response rate to FERC's survey was 59 percent. Unless otherwise noted, the data we present in our report from FERC's 2012 report and associated survey reflects information reported by those utilities responding to the survey. The data do not represent the extent of demand-response activities throughout the United States. Furthermore, our analysis of survey results to identify the primary demand-response approaches at the retail level may not match what was reported in FERC's 2012 *Assessment of Demand Response and Advanced Metering* report because FERC modified these data prior to publication, as we discuss in this report. Because these modifications were not documented, we could not verify their accuracy or relevance to our analysis. As a result, when providing data about specific retail demand-response approaches, we chose to report results from the original survey data reported by the utilities, which reflect the original, unmodified survey responses. To assess the reliability of the data, we interviewed FERC officials and performed electronic testing of the data. We found some elements of the data to be sufficiently reliable for our purposes. In other cases, we were unable to determine the quality of the data and, therefore, did not include related analyses in our report. In addition to the FERC data, we reviewed EIA's 2011 data on retail demand-response activities. We reviewed related documentation about these data and interviewed EIA about their collection, and we found them to be sufficiently reliable for our purposes. We also reviewed data collected by the North American Electric Reliability Corporation (NERC) through its Demand Response Availability Data System. These data primarily focused on operator-initiated approaches, although a report from NERC says there are plans to expand reporting to include additional consumer-initiated approaches in the future. For this reason, and because the data were not categorized in a way that aligned with the specific analysis we were performing, we did not include them in our report.

We also reviewed RTOs' data on the development of demand-response activities in their region, what consumers provide demand-response activities, and documentation on available RTO demand-response approaches. We supplemented these data with our own analysis of data on RTO demand-response resources available through the FERC survey of utility demand-response activities. To analyze the FERC data, we categorized each RTO's demand-response resources according to whether they were designed to provide capacity, energy, or ancillary services and confirmed these categorizations with the RTOs. In some cases, RTO demand-response approaches had been updated or changed by the RTOs since this information was reported to FERC.

Additionally, FERC took various steps to modify reported categories prior to reporting similar information in their 2012 *Assessment of Demand Response and Advanced Metering* report. As previously noted, because these modifications were not documented, we were unable to verify their appropriateness for inclusion in our analysis. As such, for this analysis of RTO demand-response activities, we primarily used the original survey data reported on FERC's website. In the case of the Midcontinent Independent System Operator data, FERC informed us that the data reported on its website was not correct and provided us with the corrected survey data. We interviewed FERC officials about their data and performed electronic testing of the data, which we found sufficiently reliable for our purposes. As a result, the data included in our report may not always match what was reported in FERC's 2012 *Assessment of Demand Response and Advanced Metering* report.

To assess key benefits and challenges, if any, of current demand-response efforts, we conducted semistructured interviews with a nonprobability sample of 37 diverse stakeholders with expertise on demand-response issues from five categories: trade associations and public interest organizations; academics and consultants; state government, including state public utility commissions; industry, including demand-response aggregators, large users of electricity, independent power producers, and integrated utilities; and RTOs. (See app. II for a list of these stakeholders). We selected these groups to maintain balance on key issues. Often, because of business interests, these groups have different perspectives on electricity industry issues, including demand-response activities. When possible, we used a standard set of questions to discuss topics such as the strengths and limitations of U.S. demand-response approaches, barriers to expanding demand-response activities, and steps the federal government should take to develop or refine demand-response policies. However, as needed, we also sought perspectives on additional questions tailored to these stakeholders' area of expertise and sought opinions from stakeholders on controversial key issues, for example, their views on how to best compensate consumers for their demand-response activities. In addition to interviewing the aforementioned 37 stakeholders from the five categories, we had supplementary conversations with stakeholders who did not easily fit in one of the previous five categories. These stakeholders had specialized knowledge about certain aspects of the electricity industry relevant to our study, for example, experience evaluating the competitiveness of the FERC-regulated wholesale markets. In total, we spoke with 42 stakeholders as outlined in appendix II. Throughout the report we use the indefinite quantifiers, "some," "several," and "many" to inform the reader of the approximate quantity of stakeholders that agreed with a particular idea or statement. We refer to "some" as 3-6 stakeholders, "several" as 7- 12 stakeholders, and "many" as 12-27 stakeholders. Because this was a nonprobability sample, the information and perspectives that we obtained from the interviews cannot be generalized to similar groups of stakeholders. Such an approach, however, allowed us to get more in depth responses about certain key issues related to our objectives, including the connection between retail electricity prices and the cost of serving consumers. We also reviewed current reports—including empirical studies—on demand-response issues. We identified these reports during the course of our own research, by recommendation from stakeholders, and through a literature review of retail and wholesale demand-response approaches.

We conducted this performance audit from September 2012 to March 2014 in accordance with generally accepted government auditing standards. Those standards require that we plan and perform the audit to obtain sufficient, appropriate evidence to provide a reasonable basis for our findings and conclusions based on our audit objectives. We believe that the evidence obtained provides a reasonable basis for our findings and conclusions based on our audit objectives.

APPENDIX II: STAKEHOLDERS INTERVIEWED

Category	Stakeholders
Trade Associations and Public Interest Organizations	• American Public Power Association • Compete Coalition • Demand Response and Smart Grid Coalition • Edison Electric Institute • Electricity Consumers Resource Council • Electric Power Supply Association • ISO/RTO Council • National Association of Regulatory Utility Commissioners • The National Rural Electric Cooperative Association • Public Citizen
Academics and Consultants	• The Brattle Group • Charles Goldman, Lawrence Berkeley National Laboratory • NERA Economic Consulting • Dr. Frank Wolak, Stanford University • Dr. Jay Zarnikau, University of Texas at Austin
State Government	• Illinois Commerce Commission • Maryland Office of People's Counsel • Maryland Public Service Commission • Pennsylvania Public Utility Commission • Public Utility Commission of Texas
Industry	• EnerNOC • Energy Curtailment Specialists • CBRE • Gerdau Corporation • Linde Energy Services • American Electric Power • Calpine • CPS Energy • Exelon Corporation • Southern Company

Appendix II. (Continued)

RTOs	• California Independent System Operator • Electric Reliability Council of Texas • ISO New England • Midcontinent Independent System Operator • New York Independent System Operator • PJM Interconnection • Southwest Power Pool
Others	• Scott Hempling • Monitoring Analytics • Potomac Economics • North American Electric Reliability Corporation • Vermont Energy Investment Corporation

End Notes

[1] Electricity consumers are divided into four groups: industrial, commercial, residential, and other. According to the Energy Information Administration (EIA), the industrial sector encompasses manufacturing, agriculture, mining, and construction—and a wide range of activities, such as processing and assembly, space conditioning, and lighting. According to the EIA, the commercial sector consists of businesses, institutions, and organizations that provide services, encompassing many different types of buildings and a wide range of activities. Examples of commercial sector facilities include schools, stores, office buildings, and sports arenas. According to EIA, the residential sector includes households and excludes transportation. In the residential sector, energy is used for heating, cooling, lighting, water heating, and many other appliances and equipment. Other includes uses not captured in the other three categories, including transportation.

[2] GAO, *Electricity Markets: Consumers Could Benefit from Demand Programs, but Challenges Remain*, GAO-04-844 (Washington, D.C.: Aug. 13, 2004).

[3] The price consumers pay for electricity is often a combination of rates determined by regulators and prices determined by markets. Rates are generally approved by regulators and set to recover the cost of providing a service plus a rate-of-return. Prices are market-based, determined based on the interaction of supply and demand. For the purposes of this report, we generally use "prices" to refer to both rates and prices, except when specifically discussing FERC's oversight authority.

[4] GAO-04-844.

[5] FERC is also responsible for regulating transmission of electricity in interstate commerce by privately owned utilities. FERC does not regulate transmission or wholesale electricity sales in most of the state of Texas because Texas' grid is separate from the two other U.S. grids.

In addition, FERC does not regulate transmission or wholesale electricity sales in Alaska or Hawaii because of their geographical isolation.

[6] These steps included the development of the following two orders: (1) Order 888, *Promoting Wholesale Competition Through Open Access Non-discriminatory Transmission Services by Public Utilities; Recovery of Stranded Costs by Public Utilities and Transmitting Utilities.* Apr. 24, 1996, and (2) Order 2000, *Regional Transmission Organizations*. Dec. 20, 1999.

[7] GAO-04-844. GAO, *Electricity Restructuring: 2003 Blackout Identifies Crisis and Opportunity for the Electricity Sector,* GAO-04-204 (Washington, D.C.: Nov. 18, 2003).

[8] Grid operators may provide compensation for demand-response activities to a wide range of market participants, including consumers and others. Throughout this report, we use the term "consumers" to capture the range of market participants including the consumers that reduce demand, as well as others.

[9] GAO-04-844.

10 In general, traditional electric meters measure electricity consumption on an ongoing basis, but the measurements may only be captured monthly to calculate bills for consumers. Advanced meters are capable of measuring and recording consumption on a more frequent basis, hourly or less.

[11] Pub. L. No. 109-58, § 1252(f), 119 Stat. 594, 966 (Aug. 8, 2005).

[12] GAO, *EPA Regulations and Electricity: Better Monitoring by Agencies Could Strengthen Efforts to Address Potential Challenges,* GAO-12-635 (Washington, D.C.: July 17, 2012).

[13] The types of technologies used by baseload power plants can vary by region but often include plants using coal, nuclear, hydroelectric, or combined-cycle natural gas technologies—units that utilize a combustion turbine in conjunction with a steam turbine to produce electricity.

[14] The types of technologies used by peaker power plants can vary by region but often include plants using natural gas combustion turbines.

[15] DOE, Ernest Orlando Lawrence Berkeley National Laboratory, and EnerNOC, *Addressing Energy Demand through Demand Response: International Experiences and Practices* (June 2012). This work was also supported by two authors from EnerNOC, a company in the demand-response industry.

[16] Sections 205 and 206 of the Federal Power Act, 16 U.S.C. §§ 824d -824e.

[17] Under section 205 of the Federal Power Act, FERC oversees rates for the transmission of electric energy in interstate commerce and the sale of electric energy at wholesale in interstate commerce. 16 U.S.C. § 824.

[18] Prior to the creation of RTOs, FERC approved the creation of entities called Independent System Operators (ISO). ISOs perform many similar functions to RTOs and for the purposes of this report, we refer to all ISOs and RTOs as "RTOs". However, many RTOs that originally took on names that include "ISO" have maintained them.

[19] The North American Electric Reliability Corporation (NERC), which has been designated by FERC as the principal reliability authority for the United States, oversees the reliability of key parts of the U.S. electricity grid, including establishing mandatory standards of reliability. RTOs, utility grid operators, and other participants in the electricity markets must take various actions to comply with these standards.

[20] FERC, *Assessment of Demand Response and Advanced Metering. Staff Report. Docket Number: AD-06-2-000,* August 2006(revised 2008).

[21] Public Utility Regulatory Policies Act of 1978, Pub. L. No. 95-617, 92 Stat. 3121 (1978) (codified at 16 U.S.C. § 2621).

[22] The cost of serving consumers depends on the cost of producing electricity, which is based on the costs associated with the last generating plant needed to meet consumer demand. In

restructured regions, the cost of serving consumers varies with the wholesale price of electricity.

[23] GAO-04-844.

[24] FERC, *Assessment of Demand Response and Advanced Metering*, 2012.

[25] GAO-04-844.

[26] The National Association of Regulatory Utility Commissioners represents state public service commissions that regulate the utilities that provide energy, telecommunications, water, and transportation services.

[27] Energy Independence and Security Act of 2007, Pub. L. No. 110-140, §529, 121 Stat. 1492, 1664-65 (codified at 42 U.S.C. § 8279).

[28] One gigawatt is equal to 1,000 megawatts, 1,000,000 kilowatts, and 1,000,000,000 watts. One traditional incandescent light bulb consumes about 60 watts, and a comparable compact fluorescent light bulb consumes approximately 15 watts.

[29] This scenario estimates the extent of cost-effective demand-response activities if advanced metering infrastructure were universally deployed; if consumers, by default, paid prices that vary with the cost of serving them; and if consumers were offered and used enabling technologies where it is cost-effective.

[30] In its 2009 assessment, FERC compared the size of potential reductions in peak demand from demand-response activities with the size of a peaking power plant, which it estimated to be about 75 MW in size.

[31] According to FERC officials, when developing the National Action Plan, FERC undertook a multiyear, collaborative process. FERC and DOE then worked with a diverse group of state officials, industry representatives, members of a National Action Plan Coalition, and experts from research organizations to develop tools and suggested approaches to implement recommendations made in the National Action Plan.

[32] Specifically, in a 2007 FERC Advance Notice of Proposed Rulemaking addressing *Wholesale Competition in Regions with Organized Electric Markets,* FERC highlighted the importance of demand-response activities in organized wholesale markets by describing potential benefits such as reduced wholesale prices. More broadly, in FERC's 2009 *National Assessment of Demand Response Potential,* FERC stated that demand-response resources can play an important role in operational and long-term planning, as well as providing emergency response and ancillary services.

[33] FERC, *Advance Notice of Proposed Rulemaking. Wholesale Competition in Regions with Organized Electric Markets,* RM07-19-000 and AD07-7-000, 72 Fed. Reg. 36276 (Jun. 22, 2007).

[34] Though FERC officials told us FERC efforts to promote demand-response activities have largely been in RTO regions, they also told us that FERC took some steps to address demand-response activities in orders that apply to both RTO and non-RTO regions. For example, in two orders related to transmission, FERC required entities providing access to transmission lines—for example, RTOs and utilities—to consider transmission and nontransmission alternatives, including demand-response activities, on a comparable basis when identifying transmission needs as part of their local and regional transmission planning processes. Order 890, *Preventing Undue Discrimination and Preference in Transmission Service*, 72 Fed. Reg. 12266 (Mar. 15, 2007); Order 1000, *Transmission Planning and Cost Allocation by Transmission Owning and Operating Public Utilities*, 76 Fed. Reg. 49,842 (Aug. 11, 2011). State regulators, utilities, and others have also taken steps to promote demand-response activities both in and out of RTO regions.

[35] FERC, Order 745-A, *Demand Response Compensation in Organized Markets; Order on Rehearing and Clarification*, RM10-17-001 (Dec. 15, 2011).

[36] GAO-04-844.

[37] For example, FERC addressed demand-response activities in Order 890 related to transmission planning by, among other things, allowing qualified demand-response resources to participate in regional transmission planning processes. In Order 693, FERC required that the North American Electric Reliability Corporation—the U.S. electric reliability organization—revise reliability standards so that all technically feasible resource options, including demand-response resources, be employed in the management of grid operations and emergencies.

[38] For example, in PJM Interconnection's energy markets, which operate in the Mid-Atlantic and parts of the Midwestern United States, the minimum amount of demand-response activities needed to participate is 100 kilowatts. Intermediaries may combine the demand-response activities of retail consumers in order to meet the offer minimum of 100 kilowatts.

[39] PJM Interconnection is an RTO that coordinates markets and the movement of wholesale electricity in all or parts of Delaware, Illinois, Indiana, Kentucky, Maryland, Michigan, New Jersey, North Carolina, Ohio, Pennsylvania, Tennessee, Virginia, West Virginia, and the District of Columbia.

[40] The North American Energy Standards Board serves as an industry forum for the development and promotion of standards for wholesale and retail natural gas and electricity, as recognized by its customers, business community, participants, and regulatory entities. The North American Energy Standards Board developed standards related to the measurement and verification of demand-response activities, which FERC incorporated by reference in Order 676-G. Measurement and verification involves quantifying consumers' demand-response activities. As a result, in this report, we refer to measurement and verification as quantifying demand-response activities.

[41] In section 1252(e)(3) of the Energy Policy Act of 2005, Congress required FERC to prepare an annual report, by appropriate region, that assesses demand-response resources, including those available from all consumer classes. Pub. L. No. 109-58, § 1252(e)(3), 119 Stat. 966 (2005). The report is to identify and review the following for the electric power industry: (1) saturation and penetration rate of advanced meters and communications technologies; (2) existing demand-response programs and time-based rate programs; (3) the annual resource contribution of demand resources; (4) the potential for demand-response resources as a quantifiable, reliable resource for regional planning purposes; (5) steps taken to ensure that, in regional transmission planning and operations, demand resources are provided equitable treatment; and (6) regulatory barriers to improve customer participation in demand–response activities.

[42] In years where FERC does not conduct a survey, its annual report consists of updates based on publicly available information and discussions with market participants and industry experts.

[43] The potential to reduce peak electricity demand describes the capability of consumers participating in demand-response programs to reduce their electricity use which, in turn, may reduce the system's peak electricity demand. Actual reductions in peak electricity demand indicate the amount that peak demand was actually reduced as a result of consumers' actual demand-response activities. In many cases, consumers agree in advance to provide grid operators with a certain amount of demand-response resources, which reflects their demand-response potential. However, in practice, grid operators determine, based on system needs, whether and when to call upon consumers to provide the agreed-to

amount of demand-response activities. Consumers may or may not provide the agreed-to amount of demand-response activities, but they may face a penalty if they do not.

[44] FERC's 2012 *Assessment of Demand Response and Advanced Metering* report includes data on the number of residential consumers participating in time-of-use programs. It does not include data on other consumer types, for example, commercial and industrial consumers, participating in this type of program, and it does not include data on consumers participating in other programs, such as real-time pricing programs, where prices vary with the cost of serving consumers. However, FERC provides access to these other data through data spreadsheets posted on its website.

[45] The New York ISO reported other categories of data that could potentially be combined with the above categories, including light manufacturing (10 percent) and other commercial (5 percent).

[46] ISO New England is an RTO serving Connecticut, Maine, Massachusetts, New Hampshire, Rhode Island, and Vermont.

[47] Federal agencies must obtain approval from the Office of Management and Budget under the Paperwork Reduction Act (Pub. L. No. 96-511, 94 Stat. 2812 (1980), codified at 44 U.S.C. §3501 et seq.) before requesting information from the public, such as through a survey. The Paperwork Reduction Act was enacted to minimize the paperwork burden resulting from the collection of information by or for the federal government. The act generally provides that every federal agency must obtain approval from the Office of Management and Budget before using identical questions to collect information from 10 or more persons. To obtain approval, agencies must provide to the Office of Management and Budget: (1) a description of the information to be collected, (2) the reason the information is needed, and (3) estimates of the time and cost for the public to answer the request. Examples of information collections include surveys, permits, questionnaires, and reports.

[48] GAO, *Program Evaluation: Strategies to Facilitate Agencies' Use of Evaluation in Program Management and Policy Making,* GAO-13-570 (Washington, D.C.: June 26, 2013). Additionally, in a 2012 report, GAO stated that a program can be defined in various ways, including an activity or project with an identifiable purpose or set of objectives. GAO, *Designing Evaluations (2012 revision)* GAO-12-208G (Washington D.C.: January 2012).

[49] We were not able to identify a single data source that comprehensively quantifies the extent and type of demand-response activities in retail and wholesale markets. For this reason, for information on the extent to which demand-response activities have changed over time, we provide data from FERC's annual *Assessment of Demand Response and Advanced Metering* report. These data were gathered through surveys FERC conducted and, unless otherwise noted, the data we present reflect the data reported by the 59 percent of utilities and other entities responding to the survey, rather than the extent of demand-response activities throughout the United States. In addition, most of the demand-response statistics FERC included in its 2012 report relate to potential reduction in peak demand. As a result, we have also focused our analysis of FERC data on potential reductions in peak demand.

[50] FERC does not collect data in its survey on peak electricity demand for all reporting utilities and other entities. As a result, we were unable to compare FERC's estimate of the potential of demand-response activities to reduce peak electricity demand to the actual peak demand of the utilities and other entities responding to its survey. According to data from DOE's EIA—which collects and analyzes a variety of energy and electricity data nationwide about topics such as energy supply and demand—2011 summer peak demand for the continental United States was 782,469 MW.

[51] Totals in the draft may not sum exactly due to rounding.

[52] Demand-response activities from consumers FERC categorized as "other" were responsible for the remaining 1,321 MW (4 percent) of this potential reduction in peak demand from retail demand-response activities.

[53] FERC, *A National Assessment of Demand Response Potential,* June 2009.

[54] We were not able to identify a data source that comprehensively quantifies the extent of consumer participation in various demand-response approaches in retail markets. For this reason, to analyze the extent of consumer participation in various demand-response approaches, we analyzed survey data FERC collected to develop its 2012 report. Unless otherwise noted, the data we present reflect the data reported by the 59 percent of utilities and other entities responding to the survey. They do not represent the extent of demand-response activities throughout the United States. Furthermore, the data we report may not match what was reported in FERC's 2012 *Assessment of Demand Response and Advanced Metering* report, since the agency made modifications to improve data quality prior to publication. Because these modifications were not documented, we could not verify their relevance to our analysis and instead chose to report the original survey data. More information on our approach to analyzing these data can be found in appendix I.

[55] In many cases, consumers were not able to participate in demand-response programs through their utilities. Of the 130.6 million consumers of utilities responding to FERC's 2012 survey, 16.5 million or 13 percent were from utilities that did not offer demand-response programs.

[56] The 6.0 million consumers that used operator-initiated approaches represent approximately 5 percent of the 130.6 million consumers of utilities responding to FERC's survey.

[57] Consumers identified as "other" were responsible for the remaining 1,182 MW (4 percent) of potential reduction in peak demand from operator-initiated approaches.

[58] The approximately 2.3 million consumers that used consumer-initiated approaches represent approximately 2 percent of the 130.6 million consumers from utilities responding to FERC's survey.

[59] EIA collected this information through a mandatory 2011 survey it conducted of utilities. In this survey, it asked 3,287 utilities how many consumers participated in what it called "incentive-based" demand-response approaches and "time-based rate" approaches. Examples EIA provided of "incentive-based" approaches included financial incentives, direct demand control, and interruptible prices, among other things. Examples EIA provided of "time-based rate" approaches included real-time prices, critical peak prices, and time-of-use rates, among other things. EIA does not ask those surveyed to provide more detailed information about demand-response approaches. We believe that these approaches generally align with the two demand-response approaches presented in our report: operator-initiated and consumer-initiated, respectively.

[60] According to our analysis of FERC data, 76 percent of demand-response activities were from consumer agreements to provide capacity in the future. When requested by the grid operator, for example, due to a concern about reliability, these agreements may result in demand-response activities used for energy, which are not reflected in this graphic.

[61] The Midcontinent Independent System Operator is an RTO that coordinates the markets and the movement of wholesale electricity. It operates in all or parts of the following U.S. states: Arkansas, Illinois, Indiana, Iowa, Kentucky, Louisiana, Michigan, Minnesota, Mississippi, Missouri, Montana, North Dakota, South Dakota, Texas, and Wisconsin.

[62] 143 FERC 61,218, *Order Approving Stipulation and Consent Agreement,* June 7, 2013, Docket No. IN12-15-000.

[63] FERC's enforcement office identified violations of the RTO tariff and FERC's antimanipulation rule. Furthermore, according to the FERC enforcement order, the aggregator received unjust profits. As a condition of the agreement, the aggregator neither admitted nor denied these violations but agreed to the penalties imposed by FERC.

[64] In addition, an energy consulting firm and an executive with the consulting firm were also charged with fraudulent behavior for their support of one of the paper mills. FERC commenced an action in the U.S. District Court for an order affirming a combined penalty of $8.75 million.

[65] Order 745 is currently being contested by a number of electricity stakeholders in the U.S. Court of Appeals for the D.C. Circuit.

[66] According to a PJM representative, beginning on June 1, 2014, two additional demand-response programs with fewer limitations will be available.

[67] Demand-response activities can result in environmental benefits; however, determining the net environmental benefits of demand-response activities was beyond the scope of this report. In general, the extent of environmental benefits depends on many factors, for example, whether electricity use is reduced outright or shifted to other hours. In addition, whether consumers use backup generators to offset their reductions in electricity use, will also affect environmental benefits.

[68] *National Emission Standards for Hazardous Air Pollutants for Reciprocating Internal Combustion Engines; New Source Performance Standards for Stationary Internal Combustion Engines*; Final Rule, 78 Fed. Reg. 6674 (Jan. 30, 2013), codified at 40 C.F.R. Parts 60 and 63.

[69] NERC is collecting this data through its Demand Response Availability Data System initiative.

[70] GAO-04-844.

[71] Under the basic model for designing unvarying, average retail electricity prices, all the costs of producing electricity are combined. The resulting amount is divided among various classes of consumers, for example, industrial, commercial, and residential consumers, and consumers within each class pay an unvarying, averaged price regardless of when their electricity consumption occurs. This leads to some consumers paying more and others less than the actual cost of serving them.

[72] FERC, *Assessment of Demand Response and Advanced Metering* (December 2008).

[73] Under this scenario, FERC estimated that advanced metering infrastructure was universally deployed, and consumers, by default, paid real-time or critical-peak prices. Additionally, FERC estimated that other demand-response programs were available to consumers who opted-out of the above pricing approaches. FERC compared the results of this scenario with one in which no customers participated in demand-response programs.

[74] *Advance Notice of Proposed Rulemaking. Wholesale Competition in Regions with Organized Electric Markets*, RM07-19-000 and AD07-7-000 (Jun. 22, 2007). According to FERC, "where a load serving entity offers retail customers some form of time-of-use rates, the retail customers' response to rates during a higher-priced period reduces the load serving entities' wholesale demand and helps lower wholesale prices."

[75] GAO-04-844.

In: Demand-Response in the United States
Editor: Carina Reilly
ISBN: 978-1-63321-576-4

Chapter 2

ELECTRICITY MARKETS: CONSUMERS COULD BENEFIT FROM DEMAND PROGRAMS, BUT CHALLENGES REMAIN*

United States Government Accountability Office

WHY GAO DID THIS STUDY

The efficient and reliable functioning of the more than $200 billion electric industry is vital to the lives of all Americans. As demonstrated in the 2003 black- out in the Northeast and the 2001 energy crisis in the West, changes in the cost and availability of electricity can have significant impacts on consumers and the national economy. The Federal Energy Regulatory Commission (FERC) supports using demand-response programs as part of its effort to develop and oversee competitive electricity markets.

GAO was asked to identify (1) the types of demand-response programs currently in use, (2) the benefits of these programs, (3) the barriers to their introduction and expansion, and (4) instances where barriers have been overcome. Additionally, GAO examined the federal government's

---

* This is an edited, reformatted and augmented version of a United States Government Accountability Office publication, No. GAO-04-844, dated August 2004.

participation in these programs through the General Services Administration (GSA).

WHAT GAO RECOMMENDS

GAO recommends that (1) FERC consider demand-response in making decisions about wholesale markets and report to Congress on any impediments to doing so and (2) GSA make demand-response a key factor in its energy decision making.

WHAT GAO FOUND

There are two general types of electricity demand-response programs in use: (1) market-based pricing programs enable customers to respond to changing electricity prices and (2) reliability-driven programs allow either the customer or the grid operator to adjust electricity usage when supplies are scarce or system reliability is a concern. The federal government's GSA participates in both types of programs.

Demand-response programs benefit customers by improving the functioning of markets and enhancing the reliability of the electricity system. Some recent studies show that demand-response programs have saved customers millions of dollars and could save billions of dollars more. The GSA—as only one example of federal involvement in these programs—has reported saving about $1.9 million through the participation of only a few of its buildings in demand-response programs during the past 5 years. However, GAO estimates that GSA could potentially save millions of dollars more with broader participation in these programs.

While benefits from demand-response are potentially large, three main barriers limit their introduction and expansion: (1) state regulations that shield consumers from price fluctuations, (2) a lack of equipment at customers' locations, and (3) customers' limited awareness about the programs and their benefits. Regarding prices, customers do not respond to price fluctuations because the retail prices they see do not reflect market conditions but are generally set by state regulations or laws. In addition, in recent years, moderate weather conditions and other factors have kept overall electricity prices low, reducing the benefits of participating in these programs. According to GSA, its participation in demand-response programs has been limited because it lacks specific guidance on participation and tenants have little incentive to reduce their consumption since current leases do not provide a way to share in the savings that might occur.

Two demand-response programs that GAO reviewed illustrate how the barriers GAO identified were overcome and also point out lessons on how to cultivate new programs. Lessons learned include the necessity to provide sufficient incentives to make participation worthwhile, working with receptive state regulators and market participants to develop programs, and designing programs to include appropriate outreach materials, necessary equipment, and easy participation.

In commenting on the report, FERC and GSA agreed in general with the report's conclusions and recommendations, but GSA expressed concern about one recommendation to share potential savings with its tenants.

ABBREVIATIONS

DOE	Department of Energy
FERC	Federal Energy Regulatory Commission
GSA	General Services Administration
ISO	Independent System Operator
NEDRI	New England Demand Response Initiative
NERC	North American Electric Reliability Council

August 13, 2004

The Honorable Susan M. Collins
Chairman, Committee on Governmental Affairs
United States Senate

Dear Chairman Collins:

The efficient and reliable functioning of the electric industry is vital to the nation's economy and central to the lives of all Americans. Annual expenditures on electricity amount to about $224 billion, and electricity provides the power to produce billions of dollars more in revenue in other industries. As a result, changes in the price and availability of electricity can have substantial impacts on customers and the broader economy. In particular, two events have drawn attention to the need to examine the operation and direction of the industry. The August 14, 2003, blackout that affected New York and seven other states in the eastern section of the nation's electricity system—the largest blackout in U.S. history—caused losses in productivity and revenue estimated in the billions of dollars. Just a few years earlier, in 2000 and 2001, the energy crisis in the West boosted rates for customers, forced some utilities into bankruptcy, created additional uncertainty in electricity markets, led to rolling blackouts, and demonstrated that the electricity market was subject to price manipulation.

The federal government and some states are restructuring the electric industry with the goal to increase the amount of competition in wholesale and retail electricity markets, which is expected to lead to benefits for electricity consumers. As such, the industry is restructuring from one that is characterized by monopoly utilities that provided customers with electricity at regulated rates to a competitive industry in which prices are determined largely by supply and demand. Restructuring is already under way at the federal level for wholesale markets—markets in which power is bought and sold by utilities that are overseen by the Federal Energy Regulatory Commission (FERC). As part of this process, FERC is responsible for changes to wholesale market rules, including rules to allow new suppliers to enter wholesale markets and sell electricity. FERC is also responsible for making sure that prices in these markets are "just and reasonable" and does so by the promotion of competitive markets and issuing related market rules. Restructuring of retail markets—markets serving customers—is also under way in 17 states and the District of Columbia, while other states have either suspended or delayed previous plans or do not have plans to restructure their markets. Despite some state initiatives to restructure, almost all retail prices continue to be set by regulation or state law and are not determined by supply and demand.

Whether subject to traditional regulation or the rules of a competitive market, the electric industry must manage a complex network of power plants and power lines. Since electricity travels at the speed of light and cannot be easily stored, the output of power plants must be matched precisely with demand for electricity to maintain the reliability of the network. Because of the need to precisely match supply and demand at all times, wholesale and retail markets are operationally joined. However, demand varies significantly with the time of day and year, generally reaching its highest levels on hot summer afternoons. As demand grows, utilities increase output from the power plants already supplying electricity and add a sequence of plants to meet the rising levels of demand. The last plants used to meet rising demand, so-called "peak demand" plants, are generally much more expensive to operate and generally operate the equivalent of only a few days per year. As a result, the costs of generating electricity can vary dramatically, becoming about 10 times more expensive during periods of peak demand than during periods of average demand.

In both regulated and restructured markets, the system continues to be balanced by changes in supply. Historically, grid operators maintain reliability by increasing or decreasing the amount of electricity available from power plants. The average prices customers pay are determined predominantly by the costs associated with these changes in supply. However, when prices are set by regulation or law and change infrequently, customers are largely insulated from frequent and short-term changes in the cost to generate electricity. Industry experts have long said that encouraging customers to change their demand for electricity in response to ongoing changes in its price may offer cost and operating advantages over relying solely upon changes in supply. Toward this end, some utilities and system operators have created a variety of electricity pricing and other programs that encourage customers to adjust their usage in response to changes in prices or market conditions affecting reliability of service. These programs are collectively referred to as "demand-response" programs.

According to FERC, demand-response is an important part of well-functioning electricity markets but largely missing from today's markets. Further, there is general agreement among industry experts that the absence of retail demand-response contributes to problems in wholesale markets, allowing higher, more volatile prices and the exercise of market power by electricity sellers. For example, FERC determined that the absence of consumer response to sharply higher prices in western wholesale electricity markets contributed to the financial and energy crisis there. FERC has approved proposals by several grid operators to incorporate demand-response into the wholesale markets that they oversee, but these efforts have met with limited success. As part of a broader effort to develop consistent rules for regional markets, referred to as its Standard Market Design proposed rule, FERC proposed an effort to encourage demand-response in wholesale markets. However, this broad effort was delayed because of resistance to certain aspects of the broader effort. Because its jurisdiction is largely limited to wholesale markets, FERC has said that states bear the primary responsibility for implementing demand-response in retail markets. Nonetheless, the wholesale and retail markets interact, affecting the supply and price of electricity in both.

In this context, you asked us to examine the current and potential role for demand-response programs. To address this issue, we identified (1) the types of demand-response programs currently in use; (2) the benefits of these programs; (3) the barriers to their introduction and expansion; and (4) where possible, instances in which these barriers have been overcome. In addition, we examined the federal government's participation in these programs through the General Services Administration (GSA)—a large operator of commercial office space throughout the country. GSA's involvement in these programs is discussed in answering the first three objectives.

To assess demand-response programs, their benefits, barriers to expansion, ways to overcome barriers, and the federal government's participation, we reviewed the literature, analyzed industry and participant data, and conducted interviews with state and federal officials (in FERC, the Department of Energy , and the GSA), industry experts, representatives from utilities, and customers. We examined four programs, two in states with restructured retail markets (California and New York) and two in states with traditionally regulated retail markets (Florida and Georgia). We selected these programs because they have operated for several years and experts consider them innovative and successful models. To determine GSA's participation in demand-response programs, we interviewed headquarters and regional staff and obtained information about electricity consumption and demand-response activities at 53 buildings where GSA is responsible for some or all of the electricity costs. These buildings incurred the highest electricity expenses of the about 1,400 GSA-operated buildings nationwide and represented about 40 percent of the agency's total electricity expenses in 2003. We used data from GSA's Energy Usage Analysis System and, while we did not do a complete data reliability assessment, we reviewed the steps GSA has taken to ensure the data were reliable. Further, we did limited testing of the data by comparing it with information from our interviews with GSA regional energy managers at the 53 buildings and found no significant discrepancies. We concluded that the data were reliable for the purposes of this report. We obtained information on participation and the benefits of demand-response programs for a 5-year period—1999 through 2003. We conducted our work from March 2003 through July 2004 in accordance with generally accepted government auditing standards.

RESULTS IN BRIEF

Two types of demand-response programs are in limited use: "market-based pricing" and "reliability-driven" programs. Market-based pricing programs enable customers to adjust their use of electricity in response to changing prices. For example, in a Georgia program involving about 1,600 mostly business customers, prices varied hourly depending on supply and demand. According to customers we interviewed, they turned off specific electric equipment or operated their own on-site generation during periods when prices were higher and/or shifted activities such as manufacturing to times when prices were lower. Market-based pricing programs are only available on a limited basis with only a small share of overall demand subject to changing prices. Reliability programs enable grid operators to request that customers reduce electricity use when hot weather or system malfunctions mean that demand will probably exceed supply and cause a blackout. Customers told us that they can participate in these types of programs by reducing their demand on the grid by shutting down equipment or by generating their own electricity. For example, managers of a program in New York State have established agreements that allow the utility to reduce demand substantially, with short notice. Although reliability programs are more widely available than market-based pricing programs, their use is limited. The GSA reported that 33 of the 53 buildings with the largest electricity consumption are currently registered to participate in a variety of both market-based pricing and reliability programs across the country.

Demand-response programs, according to the literature we reviewed and experts we spoke with, can benefit customers in regulated and restructured markets by improving market functions and enhancing the reliability of the electricity system. First, markets function better when prices are more closely linked to the cost of supply. This linkage can lead to lower prices and significant savings because utilities have less need to use expensive power plants to meet peak demand, price spikes caused by market conditions or by market manipulation are reduced, and industry has greater incentives for energy efficiency and other innovations. Recent studies show that demand-response programs have saved millions of dollars—including about $13 million during a heat wave in New York State during 2001. A FERC-commissioned study reported that a moderate amount of demand-response could save about $7.5 billion annually in 2010. The four programs we reviewed also produced significant savings. For example, household customers in a Florida program achieved average savings of 11 percent per year in 2002.

Second, demand-response programs may enhance reliability because they afford greater flexibility to grid operators, who can change supply *or* demand to meet their needs. Such programs reduced the number of blackouts in California in 2000 and 2001. Regarding benefits to the federal government, GSA estimated that it saved about $1.9 million from 13 of the 33 buildings that participated in demand-response programs from 1999 through 2003. The amount of these benefits has been limited to some extent because the agency has not actively participated in these programs. If GSA was able to achieve the level of participation reported to us at all of their large facilities, savings could reach $12 million to $114 million over a 5-year period, according to our analysis.

Although demand-response programs can provide benefits, they face three main barriers to their introduction and expansion: (1) state regulations that shield customers from short-term price fluctuations, (2) the absence of equipment installed at customers' sites required for participation, and (3) customers' limited awareness of programs and their potential benefits. First, customers do not respond to price fluctuations because the retail prices they see do not reflect market conditions but are generally set by state regulations or laws. This lack of response becomes important during periods of high demand, when actual costs are highest (because peak demand plants are used), but customers remain unaware of the higher costs and thus have no incentive to reduce their demand. Because retail consumers do not reduce their demand, they can also unknowingly harm wholesale markets by driving up prices higher than competitive levels. Second, most customers currently lack the necessary equipment, which includes meters for measuring when electricity is consumed and cell phones, pagers, or other mechanisms for communication with the utility. These items are not routinely required of customers, and neither customers nor energy companies are eager to pay for this equipment. Third, customers are not always aware of demand-response programs and their potential benefits. According to the operator of demand-response programs in New York State, about half of the customers that it believed were well informed about electricity matters were unaware that these programs were available to them. In addition, several factors beyond the programs' control—including moderate weather, a slow national economy, and surplus generating capacity in some parts of the country—have combined to keep overall prices low in recent years, reducing the financial benefits for participating in these programs, according to industry experts. However, they also note that such programs may be urgently needed later, when supplies are limited and prices are high. According to GSA officials, the agency's participation in demand-response programs has been limited because it lacks specific internal guidance on participation, tenants have little incentive to reduce their consumption, and other factors such as mild weather conditions have further diminished participation.

Two demand-response programs that we reviewed illustrate how these barriers can be overcome and also point out three broader lessons on how to cultivate new programs. For example, to introduce a market-based pricing program in a regulated market, a Florida utility demonstrated to state regulators that its program could offer benefits, such as lower prices to participants, without increasing costs to nonparticipants. The utility also developed outreach materials (such as a video) and provided technology that automated consumer response to prices to simplify participation. In another instance, officials in New York State overcame the barriers of inadequate consumer awareness and infrastructure by educating consumers about a new reliability program during a time when supply shortages were expected and prices would likely rise. To promote this program, the grid operator developed brochures and other sources of information that described the problems to be addressed and the potential benefits to participants. It also provided equipment to communicate rapidly and effectively when supplies were short and reliability was in jeopardy (an automated telephone notification system). More broadly, these examples offer three important lessons for nurturing such programs. First, programs with sufficient incentives, such as a clear price difference between peak and off-peak consumption, make customers' participation worthwhile. In other areas, programs have been abandoned when this price difference was insufficient to attract participants or to induce participants to reduce their usage during critical periods. Second, programs have a higher chance of success if they are begun where state regulators and market participants are receptive to the potential benefits of demand-response programs in their areas. Third, to achieve these benefits and also increase the chances of success, the design of programs should include appropriate outreach, necessary equipment, and easy participation.

We are making recommendations that FERC consider additional actions to ensure that wholesale markets are not unnecessarily harmed by retail buyers, broadly review options to implement effective demand-response, and outreach with states, among other things. We also recommend that GSA make participation in demand-response a key factor in its energy decision making, identify programs for participation, educate building operators, and align incentives so that it can more fully benefit from these programs.

We provided FERC and GSA a draft of our report for review and comment. FERC endorsed our conclusions regarding the importance of demand-response to competitive energy markets and to electricity system reliability. FERC generally agreed with the report's recommendations. GSA also agreed with the report's conclusions regarding the importance of demand-response to an efficient and reliable electricity industry. GSA stated that it agreed with the majority of our recommendations, but expressed concerns about one recommendation for GSA to share savings with tenants for successful demand-response participation. GSA stated that such sharing would not be practical because the agency, under its current leases, would assume all the risks associated with electric costs, while sharing the benefits with its tenants. We revised the recommendation to reflect GSA's concerns about risk by adding that risk should also be shared between the agency and its tenants. As revised, we believe the recommendation provides sufficient flexibility for GSA to develop practical approaches in sharing financial incentives as well as penalties with its tenants without compromising tenant satisfaction.

BACKGROUND

Demand and Supply in Regional Electricity Systems Must Be Continually Balanced and Adjusted

To avoid blackouts and other disruptions, the amount of electricity customers demand must be continually balanced with the amount of electricity power plants supply. This balance is essential because electricity cannot be economically stored. The operators of the electricity system, who oversee the complex network of thousands of power plants and power lines, collectively called the grid, coordinate this process. The continental United States is divided into three large regional electricity systems (East, West, and Texas). Changes in demand or supply within each of the three regions can affect the entire region, reinforcing the need for coordination.

Preserving this balance is challenging because customers use sharply different amounts of electricity through the course of the day and year. Typically, demand rises through the day and reaches its highest point— called the peak—in late afternoon. In some parts of the country, average hourly demand can be up to twice as high during late afternoon as it is during the middle of the night, when it is the lowest. In addition to the daily variation in demand, electricity demand varies seasonally, mainly because air conditioning accounts for a large share of overall electricity usage in many parts of the country during the summer. In some cases, peak usage can be nearly twice as high during the summer as it is in the winter.

Regardless of when electricity is used, the electricity network must have sufficient generating capacity to meet the highest levels of demand to avoid blackouts. A variety of power plants, ranging from "baseload" plants designed to operate nearly all the time to "peakers" that generally operate only a few hours per day in the summer, are used to meet demand through the day and year. Baseload plants are generally the most costly to build, but they generally have the lowest costs for generating electricity on an hourly basis. In contrast, peakers are much less costly to build but much more costly to operate.

The use of costly power plants that are seldom used results in higher electricity prices. In general, grid operators maximize the amount supplied by the baseload plants. However, as demand rises through the day and through the year, they must use plants that are more costly to operate. Because of this need to use more costly plants, the differences in the overall costs of meeting hour-to-hour demand are sometimes quite large. For example, the average cost of generation can rise tenfold from when demand is at its lowest at night to when it is at its highest in the late afternoon. Although the cost of generating electricity during peaks can be quite high, these periods are generally short and account for only a small percentage of the hours during a year. According to one expert, although the 100 highest priced hours of the year account for only about 1 percent of the hours in a year, they can account for 10 to 20 percent of the total electricity expenditures for the year. Regardless of how often or how long demand reaches its highest levels, power plants must be built to meet at least this level of demand to avoid blackouts. Because the cost of building and operating these seldom-used plants must be recovered through higher electricity prices, the need to build and use them adds directly to these prices.

Federal Restructuring of the Electricity Sector Has Expanded the Role of Competition and Markets, but States Remain Divided on Market Development

A combination of federal, state, and local governments, as well as a private entity oversee aspects of the electric industry. The federal government, through FERC, oversees the interstate transmission of electricity and the operation of wholesale markets—competitive markets in which power is bought and sold by utilities and other re-sellers. FERC has the statutory responsibility to assure that prices in these markets are "just and reasonable." As noted, FERC has historically done this by approving rates to recover justifiable costs and providing for a regulated rate of return. FERC now seeks to meet its statutory obligation by establishing and maintaining competitive markets, believing that competitive markets will produce prices that are just and reasonable.

As part of this oversight, FERC has changed a number of rules to allow, for instance, new suppliers to enter competitive wholesale markets by granting them "market-based rate authority." In essence, this authority permits suppliers to sell electricity in these markets at market-based prices. In contrast, FERC does not currently limit access of large buyers—including those who resell to retail buyers. To further competition, FERC also approves the creation of new regional entities to operate the electricity grid. In addition to overseeing the daily balancing of supply and demand, some of these grid operators also operate wholesale markets for electricity. States, through their public utility commissions or equivalent, oversee retail markets—markets directly serving customers. In this regulatory role, state commissions have historically approved utility plans for power plants, transmission lines, and other capital investments needed to supply electricity; they have also set rates to recover these costs and provide the utility with an approved profit margin. Under this arrangement, regulated electricity prices have historically been set as a single price, generally an average of the costs of serving a wide customer class, such as residential customers. Thus most of today's electricity system is a hybrid— competition setting wholesale prices and regulation largely setting retail prices. In addition, neither FERC nor the states generally have jurisdiction over electricity entities owned by cities, such as the Los Angeles Department of Water and Power, or utilities owned by their customers, such as rural electric cooperatives and local public utility districts; these entities account for about 25 percent of the wholesale market and are self-regulated by an elected board.

In addition to involvement by federal and state agencies, a private membership organization made up of large electricity providers in the United States—the North American Electric Reliability Council (NERC)—establishes technical and operational standards to maintain the reliable operation of the electricity networks. However, membership in NERC and adherence to its standards are currently voluntary, and it cannot penalize nonmembers who do not adhere to these standards. Among other NERC standards, utilities must maintain specific amounts of power in reserve in the event that demand rises to a higher level than expected or supply is interrupted, such as when a power plant has to shut down unexpectedly.

In addition to FERC's direct regulatory oversight, the federal government influences the electricity sector through the Department of Energy (DOE). Broadly, DOE formulates national energy policy, funding research and development on various energy-related technologies (e.g., energy-efficient air conditioners and refrigerators and other appliances); setting some standards for energy efficiency; analyzing energy issues; and disseminating information about energy issues to the states, industry, and the public. More specifically, DOE established the Office of Electric Transmission and Distribution in August 2003 "to lead a national effort to help modernize and expand America's electric delivery system to ensure a more reliable and robust electricity supply." This office worked jointly with FERC and the Canadian government to investigate the causes of the August 14, 2003, blackout in the northeastern United States and parts of Canada.

Both FERC and DOE Believe That Demand-Response Programs Could Address a Number of Problems

Over the past 20 years, experts have begun to recognize the potential advantages of allowing customers to see and respond to market conditions. Historically, grid operators have maintained reliable operations by increasing or decreasing the amount of electricity supplied that was needed to meet changes in demand. However, industry experts have long said that allowing customers to change their demand in response to ongoing changes in prices or limitations in supply may offer cost and operating advantages over relying solely upon changes in supply. Further, these experts generally believe that only a small amount of demand, in total, may be needed to bring about these advantages.

In this regard, FERC and DOE have said that demand-response is an important part of well-functioning electricity markets but is largely missing from today's markets. In 2001 FERC staff concluded that demand-response could reduce market power, reduce price spikes, and reduce electricity bills, among other things. Over the past several years FERC has identified problems with some wholesale markets, such as periodic price spikes and efforts by some electricity suppliers to manipulate prices. Further, FERC has said that the absence of demand-response can worsen price spikes and allow suppliers to manipulate prices, both of which produce prices that are higher than its estimate of competitive prices. For example, in its 2002 proposed market design, FERC stated that if customers are allowed to respond to high prices, then price volatility and the ability of sellers to manipulate prices could be reduced. FERC has determined that several electricity sellers in the West manipulated prices during periods when supplies were scarce and that customers did not reduce demand in response to these high prices. Over the past several years, FERC has approved proposals by grid operators in New York State, New England, and California to incorporate demand-response into the wholesale markets they operate, but these efforts are unique to each grid operator and have not yet attracted significant participation. As part of a broader effort, referred to as Standard Market Design, to develop consistent rules for regional markets to promote more efficient and reliable electricity markets, FERC proposed a limited effort to encourage consistent demand-response in wholesale markets. However, this effort to implement demand-response was delayed because of resistance to certain aspects of the broad effort.

In 2000, a DOE team studying a series of electric power outages in the U.S. found that the ability of customers to manage their demand in response to market prices was key to ensuring reliable electric service and the efficient functioning of competitive electric markets. More recently, DOE's Office of Electric Transmission and Distribution believes that demand-response could help resolve price and reliability problems and plans a demand-response initiative as part of its strategy to help modernize the grid. Further, DOE's Federal Energy Management Program has promoted awareness of demand-response programs, pointing out opportunities for electricity users to receive payment for reducing use during specific periods of time.

The Federal Government and General Services Administration Are Large Electricity Users

The federal government is a large owner and user of commercial and other building space. As of September 30, 2000, the federal government owned about 3 billion square feet of office space and leased about an additional 350 million square feet.[2] While the Department of Defense is the largest user of building space (accounting for about two-thirds of the total owned building space), the General Services Administration (GSA) is the principal landlord for the federal government, operating buildings totaling about 330 million square feet and leasing the space to federal agency tenants; it owns about 55 percent of this space and leases the remaining space from private building owners. Nationally, GSA pays the energy bills for about 200 million square feet of office space, including about $210 million for electricity used at its buildings. Almost half of this total was spent for electricity consumed in four states—California, Maryland, New York, and Texas—and the District of Columbia.

Market-Based and Reliability Programs Allow Demand to Respond to Changing Prices and Supply Shortages but Are in Limited Use

Two types of programs enable customers to respond to price variations or to supply shortages that may compromise reliable grid operations: market-based pricing and reliability-driven programs. Market-based pricing programs provide customers with information on prices that vary during the day based on the actual cost of supplying electricity so that customers can voluntarily reduce their use of electricity when prices are high. Overall, market-based programs are in relatively limited use with a small share of overall demand subject to market-based prices. Reliability-driven programs allow grid operators and utilities to avoid widespread blackouts when electricity supplies are tight by calling on participating customers to reduce demand. While reliability programs are more widely available, active participation remains somewhat limited. GSA reported that many of its larger facilities are currently registered to participate in both market-based pricing and reliability-driven programs across the country.

Market-Based Programs Transmit Information about Changing Prices, Allowing Customers to Adjust Demand, but Use Is Limited

Market-based pricing programs provide customers with prices that follow changes in electricity production costs throughout the day. We identified three general types of market-based pricing programs: time-of-use pricing, real-time pricing, and demand bidding. Two of these programs---time-ofuse and real-time pricing—provide customers with retail prices that reflect the changes in the cost of electricity throughout the day, as shown in figure 1.

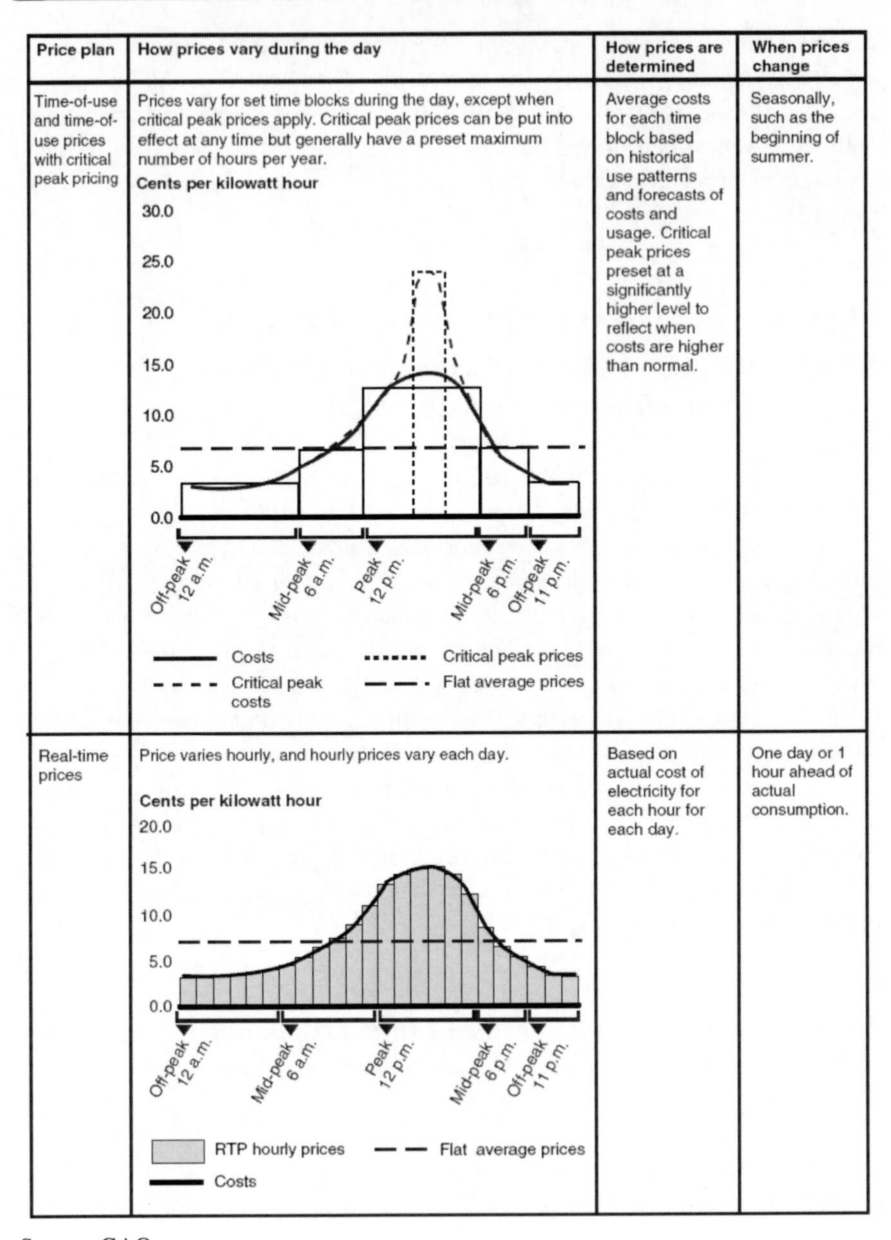

Price plan	How prices vary during the day	How prices are determined	When prices change
Time-of-use and time-of-use prices with critical peak pricing	Prices vary for set time blocks during the day, except when critical peak prices apply. Critical peak prices can be put into effect at any time but generally have a preset maximum number of hours per year.	Average costs for each time block based on historical use patterns and forecasts of costs and usage. Critical peak prices preset at a significantly higher level to reflect when costs are higher than normal.	Seasonally, such as the beginning of summer.
Real-time prices	Price varies hourly, and hourly prices vary each day.	Based on actual cost of electricity for each hour for each day.	One day or 1 hour ahead of actual consumption.

Source: GAO.

Figure 1. Illustration of Variations in Market-Based Pricing Systems.

A variation of time-of-use pricing, referred to as critical peak pricing, is also shown in figure 1. The third type of program, referred to as demand bidding, allows customers to sell back into wholesale markets electricity that they otherwise would have consumed. The prices offered by these programs differ sharply from the flat average prices that most customers face. Market-based prices can rise significantly when demand is high or supplies are short. As a result, they provide customers with incentives to reduce consumption during periods of peak demand when prices are highest.

With time-of-use pricing, different preestablished prices are in effect for predetermined parts of the day (e.g., off-peak, 11:00 p.m. to 6:00 a.m.; mid-peak, 6:00 a.m. to noon and 6:00 p.m. to 10:00 p.m.; peak, noon to 6:00 p.m.). The highest prices are established for periods such as the peak when demand and cost of supply are generally highest, based on historical cost and consumption information, and are designed to encourage consumers to reduce demand during those periods. We examined two time-of-use programs, one traditional program in California and a variation on that type of program in Florida. One industrial consumer operating a refrigerated warehouse, and participating in a traditional time of use program, explained how he adjusts his operations in response to these rates. By refrigerating some products at lower than normal temperatures during the night when prices are lower, he can turn the refrigeration equipment off during the middle of the day to avoid the higher daytime prices without temperatures rising above acceptable levels. While these responses can be useful, experts told us, traditional time-of-use prices are unable to reflect unforeseen events, such as increased demand because of extreme heat or a sudden supply shortage, which may occur if a power plant is unexpectedly shut down.

To modify time-of-use rates to accommodate these possibilities, the Florida program we reviewed operates a variation on time-of-use rates in a voluntary program for about 3,200 residential customers. Gulf Power presets prices for three periods per day (peak, off-peak, and mid-peak). However, with some advance notification, an additional price preset at a much higher level (called the critical peak price) can be put into effect at any time when supplies are tight or demand is high; however, this higher price cannot be in effect for more than 88 hours per year. An innovative control system, provided by the utility, enables customers to program the system to shut off as many as four electrical devices in response to preset price periods and notifies participants if the critical peak pricing period is in effect. The critical peak price was not used in 2003, but in 2002 the utility put the additional price into effect on 11 occasions for a total of 12 hours.

With respect to real-time pricing, prices generally vary for each hour of each day and are more closely linked to variations in the actual hourly cost of supply than time-of-use rates. There are several different ways of implementing real-time pricing programs. For example:

- Niagara Mohawk in New York State allows some of its large customers to participate in a program that prices electricity on an hourly basis, based on a forecast done the day before consumption is to occur (with about 140 customers and accounting for about 8 percent of total electricity sales).
- Georgia Power, a regulated utility, offers a voluntary real-time pricing program (with 1,600 customers and about 5,000 megawatts[3] (MW) of demand) that sets hourly prices 1 hour or 1 day before electricity use, at the choice of the participant. Under this program, participants are only allowed to pay real-time prices for the new electricity demand added since joining the program while paying their regulated rate on the rest of their demand. Officials told us that the program was designed this way to assure that customers participating in this program continued to pay for their share of the utility's existing network of power plants and transmission lines—like the rest of the utility's customers. Over time, a growing business could have a large portion of its demand priced as part of the real-time rate, which is generally lower than the regulated rate. As a result, competitors in the same business can have different electricity costs, a feature that recently has made the program highly sought after by customers. Indeed, some customers that had not experienced growth sought regulatory and/or court-ordered changes to increase the amount of their demand eligible for pricing under the real-time rate. According to one participating customer, he actively monitor prices through a Web-based system several times per day, monitors his demand, and reduces his demand if prices exceeded predetermined levels.

The third type of market-based pricing, referred to as demand-bidding programs, allows consumers to compete with traditional electricity suppliers, such as power plant owners and power marketers, in wholesale markets. While the other two types represent retail pricing efforts, demand bidding is a wholesale market effort. These programs, generally established by the grid operator or the local utility, enable mostly large customers to react to changing wholesale prices by offering bids to supply their large blocks of potential demand to the grid operator as if they were a power plant supplying electricity. We examined one such program operated by the New York grid operator, the New York ISO, and approved by FERC. In this program, customers who voluntarily sign up can bid amounts of demand reduction that they are willing to provide at prices that they determine.

They are not penalized if they do not bid; however, they are penalized if their bid is accepted and they fail to provide the agreed-upon reduction. The New York grid operator told us demand bidding was a relatively small resource for reducing demand, accounting for 1,500 MWhs, for which 24 participants were paid $100,000 or more in 2002. One participant told us that they were willing to bid when prices reach certain high levels, but they were reluctant to do so if prices were low because reducing demand generally reduced their production or otherwise hindered their business operations.

For demand-bidding programs to operate, the program operator must develop an estimate of participant demand for all hours of the year—called a baseline. According to experts, because individual consumer demand varies seasonally, in response to the economy, and for other reasons, it is often difficult to develop a baseline that accurately estimates demand. Further, because most of these customers have not agreed to purchase the electricity that they are offering to sell, some experts have questioned whether this lack of clear ownership of the electricity raises questions over property rights and opens the programs to manipulation.

Overall, the use of market-based pricing is relatively limited, generally affecting only certain types of customers and some areas and accounting for a small share of overall demand, with most customers still paying prices that are not market-based. Time-of-use pricing programs are available from many utilities, but participation is generally limited to some commercial and industrial customers. However, in some parts of the country some customers have been required to pay time-of-use rates. For example, the California Public Utility Commission requires large customers of the state's public utilities to be on time-of-use pricing plans. Real-time pricing programs are available in only a few locations, and the number of customers enrolled in these programs is generally small. With regard to demand bidding, these programs are relatively new and available only in a few locations. Even where they are available, active participation has been limited to times when wholesale prices are high.

Reliability Programs Allow Grid Operators to Reduce Demand in Response to Supply Shortages, but Use Is Limited

Reliability-driven programs allow the grid operator or utility to call on participating customers to reduce demand during periods of tight supply by shutting down equipment or by generating their own electricity. Grid operators and utilities activate these programs to avoid widespread blackouts during periods of extremely high demand or when a power plant or transmission line is shut down unexpectedly. Although enrollment in these programs is typically voluntary, the contractual agreements may entail financial penalties if a participant does not reduce demand as required by the program. We identified three types of reliability-driven programs: interruptible rates, direct demand control, and voluntary demand reduction. Some programs, such as interruptible rates, are targeted at large users such as commercial and industrial customers, while others, such as direct demand control, include residential customers.

Interruptible rate programs provide participants with a discount on electricity prices during all hours in exchange for the right of the grid operator or utility to interrupt electricity supplies if needed. Typically, the grid operator or utility requests that the participant reduce demand by some preestablished amount. Under the terms of these agreements, interruptions are generally limited to a certain number of hours per year, and the customer is provided with advance notice that service will be interrupted. Although enrollment in these programs is generally voluntary, the participant can face significant financial penalties if it fails to reduce demand when directed to do so, such as paying market prices for electricity that they consume but had agreed to interrupt.

These programs are appropriate for customers that can curtail consumption for short periods with minimal impact on their overall operations. For example, an official with one commercial participant that operated cold storage facilities also participating in an interruptible rate program told us that his operation could reduce consumption within 30 minutes of a call for interruption by turning off refrigeration units and turning down air conditioning and lighting. He said his operation could sustain a shutdown for as long as 6 hours without a problem. These programs are not appropriate for all consumers, however. Because of supply shortages in some areas, such as California, some programs have been used more frequently, and some customers realized that they should not participate. For example, when Southern California Edison needed to call on its participants frequently during the electricity crisis in 2000 and 2001, it realized that some customers, such as hospitals and other facilities, should not have signed up for the programs. Many of these entities were unable to comply with requests to reduce demand and faced financial penalties, which were later waived. Because of this experience, the company said that they now more actively limit participation and routinely examine whether participants can reduce demand to the level that they agree.

Direct demand control programs compensate customers financially if the customers allow the utility or grid operator to remotely interrupt electricity use by one or more electrical devices, such as air conditioners. In some cases, electricity may be interrupted for an hour or more, in other cases, the operator may "cycle" the equipment, shutting it down for several short periods. Generally, these programs rely on a switch installed on the air conditioner or other device that the utility or grid operator can remotely activate. By controlling a large number of small devices, the utility can ensure that, at any given time, some of these devices are turned off, thus significantly reducing the peak demand. For example, Southern California Edison operates several demand-response programs and has developed infrastructure to support them including 250,000 remotely activated switches on electrical equipment. In total, in 2003 the company had about 20 years of experience with a program that has provided about 600 to 800 MW of potential reduction in peak demand.

Finally, voluntary reduction programs are geared to large commercial and industrial customers that must meet certain requirements, such as a minimum amount of demand reduction, to participate. In one program, the New York grid operator notifies participants when it needs to reduce system demand, allowing the participant to decide how much, if any, it wants to reduce consumption from an agreed-upon baseline level. Customers are paid for any actual reduction below the baseline level. Overall, these programs provide more flexibility for customers than interruptible programs because there is no penalty if the consumer is unable to reduce its demand. However, financial benefits can accrue only if the consumer is called on to reduce demand and actually reduces its consumption. In another program, participants have signed agreements with the New York grid operator that pay them for their willingness to reduce demand. These agreements are voluntary to enter into, but commit participants to reduce demand when asked, or face financial penalties. As a result of these agreements, the grid operator is able to achieve substantial reductions in demand with 2 hours notice. These programs also require communication links between the utility and customers, as well as advanced meters so that the utility can verify and measure the consumer's actual response.

Customers told us that they reduce demand if their business situation and market prices warrant a reduction. For example, one manufacturer shuts down some processes to reduce demand and shifts workers to other tasks in the factory. In some cases, the manufacturer can compensate for the lost production by increasing output during normal work hours or during nights and weekends. However, if the factory were operating at full capacity— three shifts per day, 7 days per week—the manufacturer would need to consider whether the value of lost production exceeded the expected compensation from the grid operator. Two participants told us that certain provisions of labor contracts limited their ability to shift work to night hours, or limited the profitability of doing so, because night hours required the payment of higher wages to employees.

Reliability-driven programs are more widely available than market-based pricing programs, but participation remains somewhat limited. Many utilities offer interruptible rate programs to large commercial and industrial customers. While offered for many years, these programs were generally used to provide lower prices for some selected customers, but electricity was rarely interrupted. As a result, program operators told us that some customers on these types of programs, such as hospitals and schools, would not be able to reduce demand if directed to do so, limiting the effectiveness of some of these programs. Direct demand control programs have been offered by utilities for many years. Many customers, including residential customers, currently participate in them, allowing their air conditioners, pool pumps or other devices to be remotely turned off. Voluntary reduction programs are relatively new and only available in a few locations. Although these programs may not be activated often, officials in California and New York State told us that the interruptible and voluntary demand reduction programs helped their states enhance reliability in recent years, providing the grid operator with an additional tool to avoid blackouts and other disruptions.

Some GSA Facilities Are Registered to Participate in Market-Based and Reliability Programs

Of the 53 GSA facilities we reviewed, 33 facilities in six states and the District of Columbia are registered to participate in either market-based pricing or reliability-driven programs, or both, according to GSA officials.

These officials told us that the programs that they are signed up for are generally voluntary—they provide financial benefits when the buildings are able to reduce demand but do not include penalties if they do not respond to price changes or requests to reduce demand. Of the buildings that participate in a program, 21 facilities are registered for market-based programs such as time-of-use and real-time pricing, 7 for reliability-driven programs, and 5 are registered for both types.

DEMAND-RESPONSE PROGRAMS HAVE SAVED MILLIONS OF DOLLARS AND CAN IMPROVE THE RELIABILITY OF THE ELECTRICITY SYSTEM

Demand-response programs have saved millions of dollars and could save billions of dollars more, as well as enhance reliability in both regulated and competitive markets, according to the literature we reviewed and experts we spoke with. For example, one market-based program in California saved $16 million per year and one estimate of the potential benefit of demand-response was as high as $10 to 15 billion. These actual and potential savings occur when consumers can respond to fluctuations in electricity prices, permitting markets to function more efficiently. In addition to improving the operation of electricity markets, demand-response can enhance the reliability of the electricity system if participants reduce their demand in response to higher prices, and they provide an additional tool to manage emergencies such as supply shortages or potential blackouts.

Market-Based Programs Have Saved Millions of Dollars and Have the Potential for Even Greater Savings

Over the past 25 years, many electricity market studies have reported on demand-response programs. Recent studies have reported that several programs have saved millions of dollars and demand-response could save billions of dollars if widely implemented in the future. These studies generally fall into two categories: (1) studies of actual benefits from programs already available and (2) studies identifying benefits that could be obtained if such programs had been available to ameliorate previous crises or potential future benefits of widespread implementation.

As shown in table 1, a number of studies of market-based pricing programs demonstrate that these programs have reduced demand and resulted in millions of dollars in customer savings.

Table 1. Studies of the Benefits of Existing Market-Based Pricing Programs for Regions and Specific Programs

Study title, author, date	Results/conclusions
"The Economics of Real-Time and Time-of-Use Pricing for Residential Consumers," King, June 2001	Pacific Gas and Electric has operated a time-of-use program since 1982, with about 85,000 participants as of 2001. Consumers have reduced their electricity usage during peak periods by 18%. As of the early 1990s, 80% of participants were saving $240 per year through the program, or about $16 million per year. The utility has also benefited from the shift in demand to off-peak.
"Evaluation of the Energy-Smart Pricing Plan: Final Report," Summit Blue Consulting for Community Energy Cooperative, Mar. 2004	Community Energy Cooperative of Chicago's demand-response program had 750 participating residential customers, representing a wide variety of neighborhoods and types of homes, in 2003, its first year of operation. Under day-ahead pricing, these customers saved an average of 19.6% on their energy bills, or more than $10 per month in 2003, for modestly cutting back on consumption during approximately 30 hours of peak demand during the summer months.
"Industrial Response to Electricity Real-Time Prices: Short Run and Long Run," Schwarz, et al., Oct. 2002	Real-time pricing by Duke Power in the Carolinas induced demand reductions of about 70 MW, or approximately 8% of consumption during four summer months of peak demand. This translates into long-term savings of about $2.7 million per year for the 110 industrial customers who participated during the period 1994 to 1999.
"Customer Response to Electricity Prices: Information to Support Wholesale Price Forecasting and Market Analysis," Braithwait for EPRI, Nov. 2001	Georgia Power's real-time pricing program, with about 1700 participants representing about 5,000 MW of demand, can count on a demand reduction of at least 750 MW when capacity is constrained and wholesale markets are tight.

Study title, author, date	Results/conclusions
	On a few days in summer 1999, Georgia Power's real-time prices reached levels as much as twice as high as those seen in previous years. Prices were moderately high on several days and spiked to an extremely high level on a few days. The very large industrial customers on hour-ahead rates reduced their purchases by about 30% from their normal rate on the moderately high-priced days and by nearly 60% during the two high-cost, capacity-constrained episodes.
"Analysis for 2002 GoodCents Select Program Critical Calls," Gulf Power, May 2003	Customers participating in Gulf Power's critical peak pricing program in 2002 on average consumed 50 percent less electricity during "critical periods"—when price was higher—than did a similar group of nonparticipating consumers. Participants also paid 11 percent less in total electricity bills because their total electricity expenditures rose slower than the similar group of nonparticipants.
"Demand Responsiveness in Electricity Markets," Lafferty, et al. for FERC, Jan. 2001	Residential customers in the Wisconsin Public Service Corporation's peak-load pricing program who faced a peak price that was double the off-peak price reduced their consumption during summer peak periods by about 12%, while those facing a peak price that was 8 times the off-peak price reduced their consumption by 15% to 20% during summer peak periods. At peak hours during heat waves, consumption was reduced by 31% relative to nonpeak noncritical days.
"Responsive Demand: The Opportunity in California," McKinsey and Company, Mar. 2002.	From July 1999 through August 2000, San Diego Gas and Electric Company charged residential customers electricity prices based on regional wholesale market prices. During this period, it provided customers with the electricity wholesale price index on their monthly statements. In June-August 2000, there was an unprecedented run-up in California wholesale electricity prices.

Table 1. (Continued)

Study title, author, date	Results/conclusions
	As a result, the average customer's bill increased by 240% during these 3 months, compared with the same period in 1999. In response, during this period in 2000, customers reduced their usage by 5%.
"New York Independent System Operator (NYISO) Price- Responsive Load Program Evaluation: Final Report," Neenan Associates, Jan. 2002	The NYISO's demand bidding program provided over 25 MW of load reduction when summer peak prices were the highest in 2001. The program's scheduled load reductions are estimated to have reduced market prices by 0.3% to 0.9%. Total collateral benefits from reducing market prices are estimated to be $1.5 million in 2001. The program is expected to reduce the frequency of system emergencies and lessen the need for reliability programs.
"Framing Paper #1: Price-Responsive Load (PRL) Programs," Goldman for NEDRI, Mar. 2002	The New England Independent System Operator's, New England Demand-response Initiative (NEDRI) was used on six occasions in 2001 when prices frequently reached $1,000/MWh providing an average demand reduction of 17 MW.

Source: GAO.

As the table shows, these estimates of actual savings include savings to individual utilities and their customers as well as regional savings. For example:

- Individual programs operated by utilities located across the United States have seen reductions in demand of between 5 percent and 60 percent during high-priced hours, resulting in millions of dollars in customer savings and/or cost reductions. For example, according to a study of a long-running time-of-use program in California, in the early 1990s 80 percent of participants were saving $240 per year (or about $16 million per year in total for all participants) by cutting back on their consumption during the hours of peak demand. According to another study, Georgia Power staff could plan on participants reducing about 750 MW of power during high-priced hours, and they have seen reductions in peak demand of up to 17 percent on critical days. These savings reduce the amount of costly peak-generation equipment necessary, they said, and the program passes these savings along to its customers.

- Regional programs operating in the Northeast (New York and New England) have witnessed significant reductions in demand, which resulted in (1) millions of dollars in participant savings through price reductions and direct payments and (2) price reductions for nonparticipants amounting to millions of dollars more per year. For example, according to one study, the New York grid operator's demand bidding program reduced electricity prices by $1.5 million in summer 2001.

Our discussions with individual participants also highlighted specific savings for them resulting from the availability and use of demand-response programs. For example:

- According to a manager at a rural textile mill participating in Georgia Power's real-time pricing program, the mill reduced its purchases from the utility by increasing the output of an on-site generator during periods of high prices, for a savings of about $1 million per year. These savings allowed his mill to remain competitive while many others in the United States had shut down production and moved to other countries, in part because electricity prices were too high.
- In California, according to the manager at a three-building commercial office complex that participates in market-based and reliability programs, the complex reduced its total electricity costs by 17 percent in 2003. To achieve these savings, the facility used advanced energy controls that allowed building operators to raise or lower building temperature and lighting, as well as a thermal storage cooling system that allowed it to chill water at night and use it during the day to cool the building and thereby avoid using air-conditioning during times when prices were high.
- One residential participant in Gulf Power's critical peak pricing program significantly reduced his demand during the most costly hours and saved nearly $600 per year, or more than a third of his annual power costs, by shifting many activities from the most costly hours to off-peak hours.

As table 2 shows, retrospective studies of past crises in the West and other parts of the country that have experienced significant market problems estimate that these programs could have saved potentially billions of dollars had they been available and used in these areas. One study examined the electricity crisis of 2000 to 2001 in the West and estimated that, had market-based pricing been in place, the high prices seen in California during 2000 might have been reduced by 12 percent—resulting in a $2.5 billion reduction in the state's electricity costs. Similarly, experts have prospectively estimated that the widespread implementation of these programs could result in significant reductions in electricity costs. For example, three separate studies concluded that widespread implementation of demand-response programs could result in savings ranging from $5 billion to $15 billion, depending on the extent of participation and the costs of implementation.

Table 2. Studies of Potential Benefits of Demand-Response

Study title, author, date	Results/conclusions
Retrospective	
"The Financial and Physical Insurance Benefits of Price-Responsive Demand," Hirst, May 2002	If hourly pricing had been in place for 20% of California's retail electricity demand in 1999 and there had been a moderate amount of price responsiveness, the state's electricity costs would have been 4%, or $220 million lower. In 2000, electricity prices were almost four times higher and also much more volatile than in 1999. Hourly pricing for 20% of retail demand in 2000 would have saved consumers about $2.5 billion or 12 percent of the statewide power bill.
"Getting Out of the Dark: Market-based pricing could prevent future crises," Faruqui, et al., fall 2001	In California, during the energy crisis in summer 2000, if demand-response to hourly market-based retail prices had been in place, Californians could have reduced their peak demand by 193 MW, thereby reducing prices from peak hourly levels of $750 per MWh to $517 per MWh. For the summer season as a whole, energy costs would have been reduced on high-priced days by $81 million.

Study title, author, date	Results/conclusions
"Mitigating Price Spikes in Wholesale Markets through Market-Based Pricing in Retail Markets," Caves, Eakin and Faruqui, Apr. 2000	In late July 1999 in the Midwest, wholesale electricity prices spiked to $10,000 per MWh. If only 10% of the retail demand for electricity had faced real-time pricing and there had been a moderate amount of price responsiveness, electricity prices would have risen to only about $2,700, 73% percent less than the price actually observed. Having just a small fraction of industry demand facing real-time prices would significantly dampen price spikes.
Prospective	
Power System Economics: Designing Markets for Electricity, Stoft, 2002	Evaluating power markets broadly, the net benefits of demand with real-time pricing would be about 2 percent of the total spent on electricity. For the United States in 2003, that would amount to about $4.5 billion. This long-term estimate assumes that customers shift consumption from peak to off-peak periods, but that total consumption does not change. The estimate does not include potential benefits that accrue as a result of avoided blackouts or other service disruptions.
"Economic Assessment of RTO Policy," ICF Consulting for FERC, Feb. 2002	The potential benefits for U.S. electricity customers from adopting real-time pricing, with conservative assumptions about customers' magnitude of response and their ability for distributed generation, are estimated to be $7.5 billion annually, compared with the status quo by 2010, the first year the effects would be fully in place.
"White Paper: The Benefits of Demand-Side Management and Dynamic Pricing Programs," McKinsey and Company, May 2001	U.S. electricity customers could potentially realize benefits of $10 billion to $15 billion per year if they all participated in demand-response programs and, on average, shifted 5 percent to 8 percent of their consumption from peak to off-peak periods and curtailed consumption by another 4 percent to 7 percent.

Table 2. (Continued)

Study title, author, date	Results/conclusions
	The switch to demand-response programs would avoid 250 peaking power plants at 125 MW each to handle peak demand, for a total of 31,250 MW of peak capacity (or $16 billion to build plants used to handle peak demand). Also avoided would be 680 billion cubic feet of natural gas usage and 31,000 tons of nitrous oxide pollution per year.
"The Western States Power Crisis: Imperatives and Opportunities," EPRI White Paper, June 2001	If adopted everywhere in the United States, demand-response programs could reduce demand for electricity by 45,000 MW or about 6 percent of forecasted peak baseline usage. In California, demand-response could reduce demand by 8.7% and offset the need for new capacity by eliminating 57% of the forecasted load growth during the next several years.
"The Choice Not to Buy: Energy Savings and Policy Alternatives for Demand Response," Braithwait and Faruqui, Mar. 2001	Based on demand-response data from existing utility real-time pricing programs and actual California data for summer 2000, customer response to hourly market-based retail prices could generate demand reductions of 1,000 to 2,000 MW, reduce summer peak demand, retail prices by 6% to 19%, and produce energy cost savings ranging from $0.3 to $1.2 billion in California alone.
"The Feasibility of Implementing Dynamic Pricing," California Energy Commission, Oct. 2003	California could reduce its peak energy demand by 5% to 24% within a decade by implementing dynamic pricing and installing advanced real-time meters for all nonagricultural energy customers.

Source: GAO.

In achieving these savings, demand-response programs promote greater efficiency in supplying electricity in two ways. First, they encourage greater reliance on more efficient plants producing electricity at a lower cost and correspondingly less reliance on the plants used to handle peak demand, producing electricity at a much higher cost. This increased reliance on more efficient power plants provides the immediate benefit of lowering the average cost of supplying electricity, according to the studies we examined. This lower average cost of supply is likely to reduce electricity prices for consumers in either regulated or restructured markets. Furthermore, the use of more efficient power plants results in less use of natural gas and other fuels, potentially lowering the prices of these fuels during parts of the year. In addition, by reducing the use of seldom-used peaking power plants, the industry will need to build and maintain fewer of them overall, which will improve the overall efficiency of the industry. Since 1,000 MW of peaking power plants currently cost about $300 million to build, avoiding their construction can substantially reduce the amount of money the industry must commit to these little used plants.[4]

Second, such programs reduce the incidence of price spikes caused either by market conditions or by market manipulation. As part of its 2002 proposed market design, FERC determined that the absence of demand-response can result in periodic high prices in wholesale markets, exceeding the prices it would expect from competitive markets. Experts believe that these spikes are worsened, or in some cases may be caused, because consumer demand is determined in isolation from wholesale market conditions. Price spikes caused by natural changes in market conditions can be worsened by the lack of demand-response. For example, in late July 1999 the wholesale price of electricity reached the unprecedented level of about $10,000 per MWh for a few transactions in the Midwest, instead of the usual summer day price of $30 to $50 per MWh. While FERC determined that hot weather led to high demand, it noted that the exceedingly high wholesale prices occurred principally because high wholesale prices were not passed through to retail customers. Consequently, customers did not face high retail prices—thus they received no signal that supply costs were extraordinarily high—and did not cut consumption, which would have reduced wholesale prices. Similarly, price spikes caused by market manipulation, such as when a pivotal supplier withholds supplies in order to raise prices, can also be lessened if some consumers are able to see prices increase and reduce demand. Following the western electricity crisis, FERC determined some suppliers were able to increase wholesale prices by withholding supplies, contributing to a dramatic increase in electricity prices in California and other states. To limit the ability of producers to use their market power to raise prices and as a substitute for needed demand-response, FERC has approved various ways to control prices including price caps—collectively referred to as market power mitigation—but recognizes that these rules are imperfect solutions. Despite the presence of market power mitigation efforts, FERC has said that without demand-response prices can still exceed competitive levels. On the other hand, according to FERC officials, if there were sufficient demand-response in today's markets, the commission could significantly reduce its reliance on market power mitigation rules because markets would be more competitive. Whether high prices are caused by natural market events or market manipulation, experts believe that demand-response programs can serve to lessen the severity of price increases, if properly designed and implemented. Furthermore, experts believe that the ability to rely on more efficient plants and the ability to reduce price spikes, taken together, could significantly reduce market prices. For example, one expert estimated that a 5 percent reduction in peak demand could reduce prices by 50 percent.

In addition to immediate benefits, better aligning prices with costs offers long-range benefits because it provides the correct incentives for investments in energy efficiency and conservation or for other investments that allow consumers to reduce or avoid consuming energy during the most costly hours. These investments include thermostats to alter building temperatures during high-priced hours and equipment such as more efficient air conditioners or equipment that allows consumers to shift their demand from peak to off-peak, such as thermal or other energy storage devices. When electricity customers have more incentives to invest in such equipment, manufacturers of this equipment also have added incentive to develop and sell it. These improved incentives could result in the availability and use of more efficient energy-using equipment with substantial long-term benefits for consumers and society.

Demand-response may also result in environmental benefits in two key ways: reduced overall electricity supplied and reduced use of power plants with high pollution rates. First, to the extent that participants in market-based pricing programs reduce their consumption of electricity during peak hours and do not increase their consumption during other hours, the amount of electricity supplied may be reduced in total. In such a scenario, emissions of air pollutants are reduced. Second, in some cases, participants in market-based pricing programs may reduce their demand during high-priced peak hours, but increase their demand during low-priced, off-peak hours. These participants allow the suppliers, or grid operators, to avoid using peakers to meet demand but increase the use of another power plant. Since there are regional variations in markets and power plants, depending on the area of the country, this shift may result in the use of power plants that are more or less polluting than the avoided peaking plants. Such offsetting effects make it difficult to determine the net environmental effect. Also complicating the determination of the potential environmental benefit, some demand-response participants may rely on backup generators to supply electricity periodically. Overall, experts we met with noted that there may be net environmental benefits from these programs, but the amount of the potential benefits was uncertain and was likely to vary by region.

Demand-Response Programs Can Improve the Reliability of the Electricity System, Reducing the Incidence of Costly Blackouts

Demand-response programs can lessen the likelihood of blackouts and other disruptions with their consequent financial losses, according to the literature we reviewed. An Electric Power Research Institute study of a "typical" year's power outages and associated losses estimated that the annual cost of outages to some key sectors (industrial and information technology) of the U.S. economy ranges from $104 billion to $164 billion. In California—the state with the highest costs for outages—the costs range from $12 billion to $18 billion.[5] Similarly, the August 14, 2003, blackout affected millions of people across eight northeastern and midwestern states, as well as areas in Canada, and lasted for several days in some areas. The U.S.-Canada Power System Outage Taskforce estimated that the blackout cost between $6 billion and $12 billion in lost goods and services.

Demand-response programs enhance reliability in two important ways: (1) market-based pricing tends to reduce demand as prices rise and (2) reliability-driven programs provide grid operators an additional tool to manage the last minute balancing of supply and demand needed to avoid blackouts. First, market-based pricing programs tend to reduce overall demand during times when electricity is scarce and costly, as individual customers choose not to purchase increasingly expensive supplies. This mechanism is especially useful when demand is slowly approaching the total available supply and customers have some advanced warning that electricity is becoming more costly. For example, higher real-time prices seen by retail customers would reflect, generally within 1 hour, a power plant or transmission line's unavailability. Seeing these prices, customers tend to reduce demand and hence the amount of electricity that must be generated from power plants during the next hour. This lower level of demand, in turn, makes it easier for the grid operator to add enough supplies to meet demand and perhaps reduces the cost of doing so.

However, these programs may not be able to meet sudden needs or provide sufficient and predictable demand reductions to maintain reliability.

Second, reliability-driven programs provide additional flexibility by allowing grid operators to either increase supply or reduce demand to avoid blackouts or other disruptions. These types of mechanisms are especially useful in obtaining known amounts of demand reduction relatively quickly and sustaining demand reduction over some predictable period of time. For example, one expert told us that this type of program would be very useful if a large power plant had to suddenly shut down for safety reasons, and the grid operator found that available alternative supply sources were very costly or insufficient to meet their quantity and location needs. In this case, the grid operator might be able to maintain reliability at a lower cost by interrupting electricity service to interruptible customers for a short period of time, an interruption for which they would be paid. By this planned and compensated interruption of service for a few customers, utilities and other service providers are able to avoid unplanned service interruptions—or blackouts—for a much greater number of customers. For example:

- During California's energy crisis of 2000 and 2001, experts found that utility programs that could interrupt service were instrumental in avoiding blackouts on at least five occasions.[6]
- During a heat wave in 2001, one reliability program in New York State reduced electricity use by 425 MW on four occasions, or about 3 percent of total consumption, and achieved estimated benefits of about $13 million in reduced market prices.[7] In order to achieve these savings, the program paid selected customers $4.2 million to forgo consumption. More recently, grid operators used demand-response capabilities to aid in the recovery from the 2003 Northeast blackout, interrupting participants in order to speed a return to normal electricity service for the state's grid.

However, because some of these reliability-based demand-response programs provide for periodic payments to participants, but are used infrequently, they can be costly to maintain and difficult to justify during years when they are not needed. Nonetheless, according to experts, these programs are very important for maintaining reliability during times when electricity supplies are inadequate or demand is higher than expected. Further, several experts and program operators noted that these programs are difficult and time consuming to start up when a crisis is expected, and it is better to have them in place before a crisis.

Opportunities Exist for GSA to Benefit Further from Demand-Response Programs

GSA has achieved some financial benefits from its limited participation in demand-response programs. Of the 53 buildings with the largest electricity expenses that we reviewed, 33 reported participating in a demand-response program, and 13 of these reported savings ranging from 0.1 percent to 10.8 percent, for a total of $1.9 million from 1999 through 2003. About 72 percent of these benefits were from facilities participating in market-based pricing programs, 9 percent from facilities participating in reliability-driven programs, and 19 percent from facilities participating in both types of programs. However, while we received some estimates from GSA about its participation in market-based programs, total savings may be higher. Some building operators did not quantify the benefits of these programs and many building operators did not actively participate, even though their buildings were enrolled in them. For example, while large GSA buildings in California are registered for the time-of-use rate, as California requires, GSA staff told us that some building managers do not actively monitor price changes or take steps to adjust demand to respond to changing prices. As a result, some GSA buildings do not realize the additional savings that could result from reducing demand when prices are highest. In contrast, GSA building managers at facilities in Illinois that are enrolled in reliability-driven programs have actively participated by reducing their electricity demand, at the utility's request, in exchange for payment.

We estimate that GSA might be able to achieve substantial savings if it participated more actively in demand-response programs. Based on savings actually achieved from demand-response programs by 13 large GSA buildings (over 100,000 square feet in size) from 1999 through 2003, the median savings potentially achievable for these 13 buildings over the 5-year period, 2004 through 2008, is $6.9 million and ranges from $1.4 million to $13.6 million, depending on how actively the buildings participate, weather conditions, and other factors, and assuming that at least time-of-use programs are available. If the other 40 GSA buildings of this size were to participate in demand-response programs that provided similar savings over this period, the median additional savings are estimated to be $20.5 million with a range of $4 million to $40 million. If all 419 GSA-managed buildings over 100,000 square feet in size were to participate in demand-response programs that provided similar savings over this period, we estimated median GSA savings of $58.2 million with a range of $12 to $114 million, according to our analysis.

MULTIPLE BARRIERS MAKE IT DIFFICULT TO INTRODUCE AND EXPAND DEMAND-RESPONSE PROGRAMS

Demand-response programs face three main barriers to their introduction and expansion: (1) regulations that shield customers from short-term price fluctuations, (2) the absence of needed equipment installed at customers' sites, and (3) customers' limited awareness of programs and their potential benefits. In addition, several external factors, such as moderate weather, have kept prices low in recent years in many parts of the country, thereby limiting the financial incentives for participation. Lack of specific guidance to the tenants in GSA buildings regarding participation and the tenants' lack of incentive to reduce consumption have also limited GSA's involvement in these programs.

State Regulations Promoting the Widespread Use of Fixed, Average Prices Impede the Development of Demand-Response Programs and Efficient Wholesale Markets

Whether subject to traditional regulation or restructured markets, the costs of supplying electricity are generally not reflected in the prices that consumers see in the retail markets where they buy electricity. Instead, these prices are generally prescribed by state law or regulation as a single average price for all purchases made over an extended period.[8] Seeing no variation in retail prices, customers lack the information and the incentive to respond to the actual variation in supply conditions throughout the day and from season to season. This lack of consumer response becomes particularly important during periods of high demand for electricity, when the actual costs of its production are the highest, but customers remain unaware of the higher costs and thus have no incentive to reduce their demand. In turn, since consumers do not reduce their demand, they can unknowingly drive up the price for electricity in wholesale markets as their suppliers purchase electricity to meet their demand. This impact on wholesale prices ultimately increases the cost to consumers over time and may result in energy and/or financial crises similar to those experienced in the West. In short, the presence of such traditional retail pricing acts as an impediment to both the introduction and expansion of demand-response programs and to the efficient operation of wholesale markets.

Because retail prices remain subject to regulatory control in most cases, the introduction of market-based pricing arrangements that reflect the underlying costs of supply may not be possible without regulatory changes. In retail markets that remain subject to traditional regulation, local utilities cannot offer new pricing arrangements without first obtaining state approval. According to state utility commission staff, approval often requires demonstrating that the introduction of new pricing arrangements will benefit the participants while causing no price increases for nonparticipants. In restructured retail markets, competitive suppliers may be able to offer new arrangements that reflect costs without first obtaining regulatory approval, but the availability of flat average prices—as required by regulation or law—may continue to present a barrier to consumers switching to these rates. In addition, whether in regulated or restructured markets, because demand-response programs can reduce total electricity consumption—upon which owners and operators of the transmission system are paid—it may also be necessary to change how these entities are compensated.

Similarly, the introduction of reliability-driven programs may not be possible without regulatory and other actions by federal, state, and other entities. In general, reliability-driven programs are developed in a broader, regional context, where their success depends upon their integration with the flow of electricity throughout a region. Because electricity grids have become highly regional, with supply and demand in one part of the grid instantaneously affecting the grid across a wide geographic area, it is important for grid operators fully understand supply and demand conditions within these regional grids and to have sufficient authority to maintain reliability. Since introducing restructuring to wholesale electricity markets, FERC has approved the formation of eight grid operators across the United States that have different levels of authority and a variety of rules. Therefore, the effectiveness of reliability-based programs depends on the amount of the grid the operators control and the extent to which the operator's rules differ from the rules in a neighboring jurisdiction. As part of the changes needed to introduce reliability programs, it may not be possible to introduce several types without creating markets for them. For example, it may be necessary to make changes to allow companies to aggregate small individual demand-responses, such as residential air conditioners and water heaters, and provide a way to then sell the aggregated demand as a substitute for supply to the grid operator. To implement these changes, industry experts believe that FERC may need to change the rules used by grid operators so they can allow the creation of appropriate markets.[9]

Lack of Some Equipment at Customers' Locations Limits Use of Demand-Response Programs

Most customers currently lack the necessary equipment—meters, communication devices, and special tools—for participating in demand-response programs. Although the needed technologies are commercially available, they are not present at most customers' homes and businesses. For example, the meters installed in most homes and businesses measure only total consumption, which is generally measured on a monthly basis for billing purposes. However, most demand-response programs require meters that are capable of measuring when electricity is consumed. These types of meters generally cost between $100 and $1000, according to experts we spoke with. Additionally, experts and program operators told us that the way in which some buildings are metered is inadequate to support effective participation in demand-response. For example, regulators, program operators, and others in New York State told us that the building code did not require that commercial and residential buildings be metered individually. They explained that in New York City, which has many large residential and commercial buildings, or multibuilding complexes, some of which may comprise hundreds to thousands of individual users, a single meter measures consumption. As a result, individual customers do not pay for the electricity that they consume; instead, they pay for a share of the total electricity consumed. In these circumstances, even if an appropriate meter were installed to replace the existing meter, individual customers would have only limited incentive to reduce their consumption, since the benefits of any individual reduction would be shared among all the other customers.

Most customers also do not have appropriate communications equipment for demand-response programs. Because most customers' electricity rates change infrequently, it has not been necessary to design or implement specific communications for this purpose. However, with most demand-response programs, more timely communication is important. According to operators of programs that we reviewed, they relied on some combination of e-mail, pagers, and telephones to provide timely communication.

Finally, some demand-response programs may require other equipment. For example, in market-based and reliability programs that allow the retail energy provider or grid operator to interrupt specific pieces of electricity-consuming equipment, participants need installed switches on their electrical equipment that can be activated remotely. Installing these technologies can be costly and raises questions about who should pay for them and how best to install them. Historically, local utilities paid for and installed the meters, recovering this cost through electricity rates over several years. However, because of uncertainties about the future of retail restructuring and of the ability to recover these costs in competitive markets, utilities have been reluctant to pay for metering equipment unless cost recovery is guaranteed, which some regulators have been reluctant to do. Several experts told us that costs could be significantly reduced if the equipment were purchased and installed on a widespread basis. However, since not all customers participate in demand-response programs, it is not clear that such widespread installations are economical, even in light of the potential for reduced costs.

Customers' Limited Awareness of Demand-Response Programs and Their Potential Benefits Hinders Program Introduction and Expansion

In areas where demand-response programs are available, some customers are unaware of them or do not know how they could benefit from participation. For example, despite the widespread availability of demand-response programs in New York State, and of extensive outreach, many customers in New York State remain unaware of them, according to experts we spoke with. In a survey conducted for the operator of two programs in New York State, program operators learned that about half of the eligible customers it believed were well-informed about electricity matters were unaware of the demand-response programs. However, the same study found that the customers that were aware of the programs were highly likely to participate in them.

In some cases, the simultaneous availability of and solicitation for multiple programs can confuse potential participants. For example, California state officials told us that, in response to the 2000 and 2001 electricity crisis, many new programs were created in addition to a number of existing programs. According to one utility we spoke with, customers found it difficult to sort through the multiple options and were also were confused by utility program complexities due to multiple programs and/or changing policies and requirements.

According to program operators and industry experts, customers often do not know the specific sources of their own demand (such as various production processes and air-conditioning), when their demand is the highest, and what options exist to reduce their demand without significantly affecting their commercial operations or household comfort. For example, customers participating in the Georgia Power real-time pricing program told us that the utility staff was indispensable in initially informing them about the existence of the program, about quantifying the potential savings, and in identifying ways to reduce demand during high-priced hours.

Several Outside Factors Have Also Served to Limit the Benefits of Participating in Available Demand-Response Programs in Recent Years

Several factors have also reduced the incentive to participate in demand-response programs over the past several years. These include (1) moderate weather across most of the country over the past couple of years that has limited overall and peak demand; (2) a slow national economy, which has limited overall demand; and (3) many new power plants in some parts of the country have increased supply and lowered costs in those areas. Consequently, prices have moved downward overall. However, experts note that these types of programs may be urgently needed when supplies are limited and prices are high.

According to participants that we met with, they hoped to benefit from their ability to reduce demand when prices were high and, in some cases, increase demand when prices were low. Participants told us that although they signed up for demand-response programs, they often would not actively participate unless prices were high enough to offset the costs of shutting down. Some businesses said they may not continue to participate unless they could demonstrate the financial benefits of doing so on a regular basis to senior managers, either through higher prices or through some ongoing payment for their willingness to reduce demand if needed. Recognizing this problem, program operators, grid operators, and others said that the persistence of low prices could imperil demand-response programs. For example, in the parts of the West where prices have historically been generally low, there was only limited demand-response capability outside of California. However, this capability became urgently needed during the crisis of 2000 and 2001. Because these programs are difficult to start up, particularly during a crisis, little additional demand-response was available.

GSA's Participation in Demand-Response Programs Has Been Limited

According to GSA officials, participation in demand-response programs has been limited for the following reasons:

- *GSA lacks specific guidance on how to participate.* While GSA provides guidance regarding participation in reliability-driven programs, information regarding market-based pricing programs is limited. For example, a regional energy manager we spoke with was not generally familiar with market-based pricing programs and thought that backup generation was required to participate. Another regional energy manager told us that he relied on information provided by the local utility and grid operator to provide the information he used to make decisions on whether to participate in these programs.
- *Federal agency tenants have little incentive to reduce their consumption.* According to GSA officials, current leases require a fixed monthly payment from federal agency tenants, which does not provide a way to share any savings from demand reduction efforts or to pass on the higher costs to agencies creating higher demand during high cost periods. Therefore, tenants do not have incentives to seek opportunities for the electricity savings that could be realized from participation in demand-response programs.

In addition, the need to reduce demand has been limited in recent years. As with other customers, GSA officials have not seen high electricity prices because of such factors as moderate weather. Consequently, GSA officials told us that they have had difficulty maintaining interest in reliability-based programs among their clients or in recruiting new ones.

CERTAIN PROGRAMS SHOW HOW BARRIERS WERE OVERCOME AND PROVIDE LESSONS ON HOW TO CULTIVATE NEW PROGRAMS

Certain demand-response programs that we reviewed illustrate how the barriers we identified were overcome and also point out three broader lessons on how to cultivate new programs.

Two Programs Illustrate How to Overcome Barriers

To overcome regulatory barriers, Gulf Power, a regulated utility in the panhandle of Florida, introduced its GoodCents Select market-based pricing program by receiving regulatory approval to offer it as a voluntary program. The utility demonstrated to state regulators that its program could offer benefits such as lower overall electricity costs and additional services to participants without raising prices for or otherwise harming nonparticipants. In general, state regulators told us that they review the impact of programs on the electricity rates of nonparticipants, which is referred to as the rate impact test. This test compares the avoided costs, including costs to construct power plants and transmission lines as well as costs to operate and maintain new facilities, with the costs of operating the program. In the case of the demand-response program that we reviewed, they approved the program proposed by the utility because of its benefits for both participants and nonparticipants.

Gulf Power also overcame the barrier of inadequate equipment by installing an innovative package of new technologies, including a computerized controller, called a "gateway" that integrates the metering, communication, and switches to control demand. Figure 2 illustrates this system. The programmable thermostat receives and displays information about the current electricity price period (e.g., peak prices) and allows customers to preprogram demand reductions for up to four appliances based on time-ofday or in response to changes in prices, or both. The switches are automatically triggered if the preprogrammed criteria are met such as if high critical peak prices are in effect. For example, customers can choose to shut off the heat pump, air conditioner, pool pump, or hot water heater if prices reach a certain point or other events occur. By automating demand reduction, this program allows customers to avoid consuming costly electricity, even if they are not actually present to monitor or turn off the equipment.

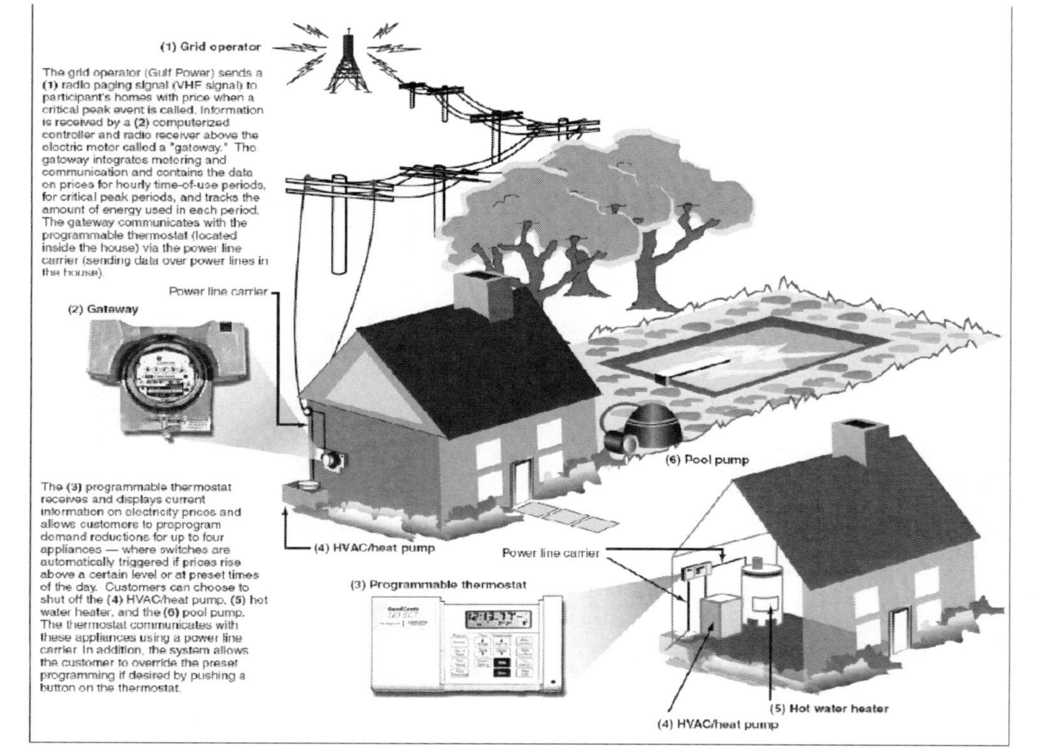

Source: GAO analysis and illustration based on Gulf Power information; photos (2) and (3) Gulf Power.

Figure 2. Gulf Power's Energy Control System for Residential Participants in GoodCents Select.

However, this system also allows the consumer to override the preset programming if desired; for example to operate the air-conditioning if they are home during the day. The data on electricity usage is sent periodically via an integrated telephone line. Utility officials noted that installing meters and related equipment for their programs costs, on average, $600 to $700 per customer. In addition, because Gulf Power was able to demonstrate to regulators that the program provided benefits to nonparticipants, it was possible to have some of the cost of the equipment paid for by a state mechanism used to fund energy efficiency and other similar programs. The cost-sharing required participants to pay 60 percent and all ratepayers to pay 40 percent of the costs. These technologies had the added benefit of making participation easy, a consideration that was important to customers.

Gulf Power also overcame the barrier of limited customer awareness through advertising and providing additional services that customers valued, such as whole house surge suppression and power outage notification, for a fee of $4.95 per month. This charge also enables the utility to recoup some of its expenses. Gulf Power utilized mass marketing techniques to make consumers aware of the program and to provide basic information about the advantages available to participants. Further, the utility provided a detailed information package to interested customers and actively followed up with telephone and other contacts. Utility officials told us that customers require substantial education about the program's benefits, its basic features, and its ease of access to make the program successful. Residential customers, according to these officials, must be convinced that they will not be worse off financially and that they can achieve savings without substantially reducing their quality of life. In addition to the services provided by the innovative package of metering and other technologies, participants also received other services that they valued as part of their participation.

In New York State, the grid operator overcame barriers to establish both a market-based pricing program and a reliability-driven program primarily targeting commercial and industrial customers. In the summer of 2000, grid operators, utilities, and others expected supply shortages and quickly established these new programs to address these shortages.

The New York grid operator overcame the regulatory barriers by convincing the state regulators and FERC to make changes needed to establish the programs. These included the creation of an electronic trading marketplace so participants could offer their demand reductions to the grid operator at a certain price. State regulatory officials told us that they and FERC were open to considering the regulatory changes because there were no other options for quickly adding new power.

The New York grid operator overcame the barrier of inadequate equipment by identifying a state-funded entity to share the cost of installing the needed equipment. The program received financial support from the New York State Energy Research and Development Authority for installing needed equipment such as meters that can measure hourly consumption. This organization was allowed to provide as much as 70 percent of the cost of the meters, but it generally paid about 40 to 45 percent of the costs. The grid operator told us that the availability of this money made the customer's decision to participate easier because costs were lower. The ISO also developed an automated telephone notification system, introduced in 2003, to replace the previous nonautomated process, which was described as time-consuming and inefficient. New York grid operators used the new system for the first time in August 2003 in conjunction with the blackout.

The grid operator overcame the barrier of inadequate customer awareness by starting the program during a time when supply shortages were expected and by widely publicizing the program's availability and its potential benefits. The grid operator provided brochures and other sources of information that identified the growing threat posed by the tight electricity supplies, the benefits of participating in the program, the role of participants, and the rules under which the program operated. In addition, state officials hosted a series of workshops that boosted awareness of the program and the need for demand-response. Enrollment in the program has grown substantially from its inception; in 2002 there were about 1,700 participants accounting for about 1,500 MW of demand. Industrial customers have also formed a trade association that has helped identify ways to improve the program.

Successful Demand-Response Programs Offer Three Important Lessons for Nurturing Further Programs

The demand-response programs that we reviewed offer important lessons for such programs to succeed. First, programs with sufficient incentives make customers' participation worthwhile. For example, Gulf Power's market-based pricing program provides a more than sevenfold difference between the lowest and the highest prices, depending on the time of day and season. Exposure to this great a difference in prices and the savings that result from adjusting demand accordingly provide a strong incentive for participation. In contrast,

Puget Sound Energy began a somewhat similar program that was ultimately unsuccessful because the price differences with the regulated program were only about 20 percent different—too small to induce customers to change their consumption,[10] according to studies we reviewed.

Second, programs are more likely to succeed if state regulators and market participants are receptive to the potential benefits of demand-response programs in their areas. In both Florida and New York State, certain market factors made demand-response especially appealing. In Florida, Gulf Power's customer base is predominantly residential and prone to sharp variation in daily and seasonal demand because of air-conditioning. In presenting their case to state regulators, utility officials, demonstrated that the avoided costs of adding new capacity were greater than the costs of introducing a market-based pricing program. Similarly, in New York State, state officials recognized the potential for supply shortages, the difficulty of adding new capacity, and the benefits of developing a reliability-driven program as an alternative.

Third, to achieve these benefits and increase the chances of success, the design of programs should consider appropriate outreach, the introduction of necessary equipment, and the ease with which customers can participate. The programs discussed here have demonstrated that these factors are also critical to success.

CONCLUSION

The goal of restructuring the electricity industry is to increase the amount of competition in wholesale and retail electricity markets. While wholesale market prices are now largely determined by supply and demand in those markets, retail demand does not generally respond to market conditions because of key barriers discussed in this report, especially the presence of flat, average prices generally set by states. These prices serve to insulate consumers from market conditions and prevent them from potentially choosing to reduce demand when prices are rising dramatically or when grid reliability is a concern. As such, retail consumers—as was the case in California—can unknowingly drive up wholesale market prices because they continue to consume as much as or more electricity than normal even when demand could exceed available supplies. Thus, this hybrid system— competition setting wholesale prices and regulation setting retail prices— results in electricity markets that do not work as well as they could.

This hybrid system also makes it difficult for FERC to assure the public that wholesale prices are "just and reasonable." While electricity markets are subject to divided jurisdiction, it is clear that these markets remain operationally joined; actions in one market affect the other. FERC has previously determined that actions in retail markets, particularly when consumers do not respond to market conditions, can cause prices in wholesale markets to exceed competitive levels. Such outcomes are not desirable or consistent with FERC's responsibility for wholesale prices. Thus, FERC may have to take additional steps—within its jurisdictional boundaries—to ensure that competitive wholesale markets are not, unknowingly or unnecessarily, harmed by retail buyers.

It is clear that connecting wholesale and retail markets through demand response would help competitive electricity markets function better and enhance the reliability of the electric system, thus potentially delivering large benefits to consumers. Overcoming existing barriers will not be easy, however. Capturing these benefits will require leadership, collaboration, and action on the part of FERC, interested state regulatory commissions, and market participants in order to develop electricity markets that are truly competitive. Without these efforts to incorporate demand-response in today's markets, prices will be higher than they could be, the incidence of price spikes caused by either market conditions or by market manipulation will be greater, and industry will have less incentive for energy efficiency and other innovations, among other things.

To date, GSA has benefited from participation in demand-response programs, but clearly could do more. As a large customer with buildings located across the country, GSA is uniquely situated to benefit from demand-response programs and to provide a benefit to local electricity markets. While it has signed up for some programs, GSA could participate more actively by adjusting its energy consumption in response to prices and/or emergencies when asked—without compromising the operation of its buildings or tenants. To the extent that GSA does so, it could further reduce its annual electricity spending, possibly benefit the broader electricity market, and provide an opportunity for the federal government to lead by example.

Recommendations for Executive Action

We recommend that the Chairman of the Federal Energy Regulatory Commission take the following three actions:

- Because the lack of demand-response can result in wholesale prices that are not consistent with competitive outcomes and may not be "just and reasonable," we recommend that the Chairman consider the presence or absence of demand-response programs when: (1) determining whether to approve new market designs or approve changes to existing market designs, (2) considering whether to grant market-based rate authority, and (3) determining whether to allow some buyers to participate in wholesale markets. As part of this process, FERC should consider its authority to use this information in making decisions on these matters. If there is inadequate demand responsiveness and FERC determines that it has authority, it should not approve these designs, authorities, or participation until such time as there is some combination of price and/or reliability based demand-response to assure that prices will be just and reasonable. If FERC determines that its authority is not sufficient to take such action, it should seek this authority from Congress.
- In reporting to Congress, the Chairman should identify the options that may have potentially large benefits and are cost-effective for achieving consumer response, as well as statutory or other impediments to putting these options into practice.
- Because the development of demand-response programs depends upon there being markets where these services can be sold, the Chairman should encourage, where reasonable, equal consideration of supply and demand when approving or changing market designs.

In implementing these recommendations, it is important that the Commission continue working with system operators, regional entities, and interested state commissions, and market participants to develop compatible regional market rules and policies regarding demand-response. FERC should use these outreach efforts to identify regions of the country where demand-response programs are most urgently needed and where grid operators, state regulatory officials, and market participants are amenable to the collaborative introduction of regionwide demand-response programs. As part of its efforts, FERC should also engage the Department of Energy in its examination of demand-response options and involve the department in its outreach efforts, thus leveraging its expertise in identifying cost-effective technologies and its relationships with state, industry, and consumer groups.

Because demand-response programs offer potential financial benefits to the federal government and to demonstrate the federal government's commitment to improving the functioning of electricity markets, we recommend that, for locations where the General Services Administration has significant energy consumption, its Administrator take the following four actions:

- Require regional energy managers to identify what demand-response programs are available to them, require building operators to determine whether they could actively participate in the programs, and quantify the benefits of that participation.
- Develop guidance that clearly articulates to the regional offices that participation in demand-response programs should be considered as part of the energy decisions that they make.
- Require (1) guidance on specific measures that building operators can take to respond to market-based programs, similar to the guidance that they provide for responding to emergencies and (2) training on evaluating how to maximize benefits from participation in these programs.
- Clarify the incentives for participation by defining how the GSA, its building operators, and its federal agency tenants will share the benefits and risks of participating in these programs through its leases.

AGENCY COMMENTS AND OUR EVALUATION

We provided FERC and GSA a draft of our report for review and comment. The Chairman of FERC endorsed our conclusions regarding the importance of demand-response to competitive energy markets and to electricity system reliability. The Chairman also generally agreed with the report's recommendations. In response to one recommendation, the Chairman agreed to consider conditioning market-based rate authority on the presence of sufficient demand-response, but noted FERC uncertainty as to whether it can require such a condition or that such conditioning would be workable, given current policy that separates wholesale and retail functions. Our recommendation, however, has a precedent in a similar state jurisdictional issue—that of the construction of new power plants. In this instance, FERC approved a mechanism, commonly known as "capacity markets," that created an additional market for power plants and serves as a signal for when they are needed. In the same way, our recommendation, if properly implemented, could create such a market for demand-response as well as serve as a complementary signal for new capacity. FERC also provided several general and clarifying comments or suggestions that we incorporated as appropriate.

GSA agreed with the report's conclusions regarding the importance of demand-response to an efficient and reliable electricity industry. GSA also stated that it agreed with the majority of our recommendations, but it expressed some concern about one of them. Overall, its comments focused on concerns about risk, especially in the form of financial penalties that GSA may incur through participation in demand-response programs. GSA also commented on the broad risks regarding price stability and power reliability that pervade the transition from regulated to restructured electricity markets. As such, GSA expressed concern about the fourth recommendation for GSA to define how benefits from successful demand-response participation will be shared with tenants. With this broad concern regarding risk to GSA in mind, GSA expressed the view that such sharing would not be practical because the agency would bear the risk while tenants reaped the rewards and because the savings to be shared are of a short-term nature. We revised the recommendation to reflect GSA's concern by adding that risk should be shared between the agency and its tenants. As revised, we believe the recommendation provides sufficient flexibility for GSA to develop practical approaches for sharing financial incentives as well as penalties with its tenants to encourage participation in demand-response programs. However, we note that as the electricity market places greater emphasis on competition, consumers such as GSA and the federal agencies that it serves will face greater price volatility. Consequently, efforts to manage this greater price volatility by developing demand-response capabilities will be an important element in managing GSA's operating costs.

Sincerely yours,

Jim Wells
Director,
Natural Resources and Environment

APPENDIX I: SCOPE AND METHODOLOGY

To assess demand-response programs, their benefits, barriers to expansion, ways to overcome barriers, and the federal government's participation, we conducted an extensive review of the literature; analyzed industry and participant data on the performance of the programs, where such data was available to us; and conducted interviews with state and federal officials (in the Federal Energy Regulatory Commission [FERC], the Department of Energy, and the General Services Administration [GSA]) and the Edison Electric Institute, a trade association representing large electricity providers.

To provide insights on the operation and experience of several current programs, we also examined programs in four states in greater detail: two in states with restructured retail markets (California and New York State) and two in states with traditionally regulated retail markets (Georgia and Florida). We selected these programs because they have operated for several years and experts consider them innovative and successful models. In particular, we examined the following programs:

- In California, we examined programs operated by one large electricity provider and several programs operated by others. We examined two programs operated by Southern California Edison: time-of-use rates for large customers, interruptible rates for large customers, and and direct interruptions to the operation of specific electrical devices, such as air conditioners at customers' homes and/or businesses. In addition, we discussed a range of programs operated by the state grid operator (the California Independent System Operator [ISO]), and the state created in response to the electricity crisis in 2000 and 2001. We interviewed officials at Southern California Edison, the state public utility commission, the California ISO, the California Energy Commission, California Power Authority, and Pacific Gas and Electric. In addition, we met with four customers that participated in programs operated by Southern California Edison.
- In New York State, we examined programs operated by one large electricity provider and by the state grid operator. We examined a real-time pricing program implemented by Niagara Mohawk that provides day-ahead hourly prices against which actual consumption is billed. We also examined programs operated by the state grid operator (New York ISO)—one market-based pricing program and two reliability programs. We examined the New York ISO demand-bidding program (called the Day-Ahead Demand-Response Program). We examined one reliability program (called the Emergency Demand-Response Program) that pays participants who reduce demand when reliability is at risk. We also examined a reliability program (called

the Special Case Resources) that requires participants to sign agreements in advance to reduce demand whenever requested and pays them for doing so. In our report, we combine our discussion of these two reliability programs. We also interviewed staff from Niagara Mohawk, the New York ISO, the New York State Energy Research and Development Authority, the New York Public Service Commission, and a consultant who annually reviews the performance of programs run by the New York ISO. In addition, we met with four customers that participate in programs operated by the New York ISO and/or Niagara Mohawk.

- In Georgia, we examined a real-time pricing program operated by Georgia Power, a regulated utility. We also interviewed staff at Georgia Power, the Georgia Department of Natural Resources—Environmental Protection Division, and the Georgia Public Service Commission. In addition, we met with two customers that have participated in the Georgia Power program.
- In Florida, we examined a critical peak-pricing program (GoodCents Select) operated by Gulf Power, a regulated utility. We also interviewed staff at Gulf Power, the Florida Office of the Public Counsel, the Florida Energy Office, and the Florida Public Service Commission. In addition, we met with one residential participant in the program.

To determine GSA's participation in demand-response programs, we interviewed GSA staff located in the headquarters' Energy Center of Expertise and in GSA's 11 regional offices and obtained information about electricity consumption at about 1,400 facilities where GSA pays for electricity. In addition, we obtained information about demand-response activities at 53 large GSA buildings. These buildings incurred the highest electricity expenses of the about 1,400 GSA-operated buildings nationwide and represented about 40 percent of the agency's total electricity expenses in 2003. We obtained information on participation and the benefits of demand-response programs for a 5-year period—1999 through 2003. To estimate the potential benefits of GSA's more widespread and active participation in demand-response programs, we used information on GSA's participation and benefits from the 53 large buildings for 1999 through 2003 to estimate the potential benefits to large GSA-controlled buildings for 2004 through 2008. Specifically, we based our estimate of possible future GSA savings from demand-response programs on historical data on savings by GSA buildings participating in demand-response, the degree to which these buildings participated, and weather conditions, which we obtained from GSA and other sources. To account for variations in the factors affecting benefits, a Monte Carlo simulation was performed. In this simulation, values were randomly drawn 1,500 times from probability distributions characterizing possible values for participation rates, degree of participation, and weather conditions. The simulation resulted in forecasts of possible future savings from demand-response program participation by GSA.

In developing our report we also met with 20 experts, who have extensive experience with demand-response programs. These individuals are listed in appendix II.

We conducted our work from March 2003 through July 2004 in accordance with generally accepted government auditing standards.

Appendix II: Selected Experts Interviewed

This appendix lists the 20 experts we interviewed on the issues surrounding demand-response programs. Their listing here does not indicate their agreement with the results of our work.

1) Severin Borenstein, University of California-Berkeley
2) Steve Braithwait, Christensen Associates
3) Richard Cowart, Regulatory Assistance Project
4) Larry DeWitt, Pace University School of Law
5) Ahmed Faruqui, Charles River Associates
6) Steve George, Charles River Associates
7) Joel Gilbert, Apogee Interactive
8) Charles Goldman, Lawrence Berkeley National Laboratory
9) Eric Hirst, Consulting in Electric-Industry Restructuring
10) Jerry Jackson, Jerry Jackson Associates Ltd.
11) Lynne Kiesling, Northwestern University
12) Chris King, E Meter Corporation
13) Roger Levy, Levy Associates
14) Amory Lovins, Rocky Mountain Institute
15) Bernie Neenan, Neenan Associates
16) Michael O'Sheasy, Christensen Associates
17) Steven Rosenstock, Edison Electric Institute
18) Larry Ruff, Charles River Associates

19) Vernon Smith, George Mason University
20) William Smith, Electric Power Research Institute

End Notes

[1] In some instances, state public utility commissions have allowed the use of time-of-use rates, or other time-differentiated pricing, but these cases are limited.

[2] U.S. General Services Administration, *Summary Report of Real Property Owned by the United States Throughout the World* (Washington, D.C.: June 2001). We have reported that the governmentwide real property data that GSA compiles—often referred to as the worldwide inventory—have been unreliable and of limited usefulness. However, these data provide the only available indication of the size and characteristics of the federal real property inventory. For more information, see U.S. General Accounting Office, *Federal Real Property: Better Governmentwide Data Needed for Strategic Decisionmaking*, GAO-02-342 (Washington, D.C.: Apr. 16, 2002).

[3] A watt is a measure of electrical power, or work. A kilowatt (KW) is 1,000 watts. A megawatt (MW) is 1,000,000 watts. One megawatt is equal to the demand of about 750 homes. A kilowatt used for 1 hour is equal to 1 kilowatt-hour (KWh). A megawatt used for 1 hour is equal to 1 megawatt-hour (MWh).

[4] According to industry data (Platts PowerDAT), from 1998 through 2003, power plants in the United States with a total generating capacity of between 84,000 MW and 134,000 MW operated 10% or less of the time. In 2003, these seldom used plants accounted for about 14% of the total installed capacity in the United States.

[5] "The Cost of Power Disturbances to Industrial and Digital Economy Companies," Consortium for Electric Infrastructure to Support a Digital Society, EPRI and the Electricity Innovation Institute (June 2001).

[6] Goldman, et al., estimated that demand-response during this period avoided between 50 and 160 hours of rolling blackouts ("California Customer Load Reductions during the Electricity Crisis: Did They Help to Keep the Lights On?" LBL [May 2002]).

[7] In addition to these savings, the utility reduced its hedging costs by $3.9 million, and all customers together saved $20 to $40 million from the lowered likelihood of blackouts.

[8] U.S. General Accounting Office, *Lessons Learned from Electricity Restructuring: Transition to Competitive Markets Underway, but Full Benefits Will Take Time and Effort to Achieve*, GAO-03-271 (Washington, D.C.: Dec. 17, 2002). As noted earlier, only a small amount of demand, in total, may be needed to deliver the benefits of demand-response. Only a few customers need to be responsive to varying prices for there to be "adequate" levels of demand-response in markets. Customers would be free to choose between (1) paying varying prices, with varying monthly bills, and (2) paying slightly more, on average, in order to be guaranteed flat monthly prices reflecting the average cost of serving them over a longer period of time. Customers willing to respond to varying prices would not pay for a "flat price" guarantee.

[9] Because NERC establishes technical and operational standards, including the need to maintain certain levels of reserves, it may also be necessary to change rules to allow demand-response options to be counted in measuring whether grids are being operated reliably.

[10] One study calculated that, if an average customer shifted all usage out of expensive periods and into the economy period, savings would amount to only $4.65 per month.

In: Demand-Response in the United States
Editor: Carina Reilly
ISBN: 978-1-63321-576-4

Chapter 3

2013 ASSESSMENT OF DEMAND RESPONSE AND ADVANCED METERING*

Federal Energy Regulatory Commission

INTRODUCTION

This report is the Federal Energy Regulatory Commission staff's (Commission staff's) eighth annual report on demand response and advanced metering. It fulfills a requirement of the Energy Policy Act of 2005 (EPAct 2005) section 1252(e)(3)[1] that the Federal Energy Regulatory Commission (FERC or Commission) prepare and publish an annual report, by appropriate region, that assesses electricity demand response resources, including those available from all consumer classes.[2]

Since 2006, Commission staff has published a series of annual reports assessing demand response and advanced metering in the U.S. In support of these reports, the FERC staff has conducted comprehensive nationwide surveys every other year. For reports in intervening years, including this report, the information is based on publicly-available information and discussions with market participants and industry experts.

* This is an edited, reformatted and augmented version of a Staff Report issued October 2013.

Based on the information reviewed, it appears that:

- Data from several sources show that the penetration of advanced meters is up, from approximately nine percent in 2009 to nearly 25 percent in late 2011/early 2012;[3]
- Since 2009, demand response potential in organized markets operated by the Regional Transmission Organizations (RTOs), Independent System Operators (ISOs), and Electric Reliability Council of Texas (ERCOT) increased by more than 4.1 percent; and,
- Demand response resources made significant contributions to balancing supply and demand during system emergencies for several RTOs and ISOs in the summer of 2013.

The report is organized according to the six requirements included in section 1252(e)(3) of EPAct 2005, which directs the Commission to identify and review:

(A) saturation and penetration rate of advanced meters and communications technologies, devices and systems;
(B) existing demand response programs and time-based rate programs;
(C) the annual resource contribution of demand resources;
(D) the potential for demand response as a quantifiable, reliable resource for regional planning purposes;
(E) steps taken to ensure that, in regional transmission planning and operations, demand resources are provided equitable treatment as a quantifiable, reliable resource relative to the resource obligations of any load-serving entity, transmission provider, or transmitting party; and
(F) regulatory barriers to improved customer participation in demand response, peak reduction and critical period pricing programs.

Each of the above requirements is addressed below in a separate section. Within that section, information concerning relevant state, federal and industry activities is also provided.

Table 1. Estimates of Advanced Meter Penetration Rates

Source of No. of Advanced Meters	Reference Date (Month/Year)	Number of Advanced Meters (millions)	Total Number of Meters (millions)	Advanced Meter Penetration Rates (advanced meters as a % of total meters)
2008 FERC Survey	Dec 2007	6.7[1]	144.4[1]	4.7%
2010 FERC Survey	Dec 2009	12.8[2]	147.8[2]	8.7%
2012 FERC Survey	Dec 2011	38.1[3]	166.5[3]	22.9%
EIA-861 Annual Survey	Dec 2011	37.3[4]	151.7[4]	24.6%
Institute for Electric Efficiency	May 2012	35.7[5]	151.7[4]	23.5%
Innovation Electricity Efficiency	July 2013	45.8[6]	151.7[4]	30.2%

Sources:

[1] FERC, Assessment of Demand Response and Advanced Metering staff report (December 2008).

[2] FERC, Assessment of Demand Response and Advanced Metering staff report (February 2011).

[3] FERC, Assessment of Demand Response and Advanced Metering staff report (December 2012).

[4] Energy Information Administration, Form EIA-861 Data File 2 and Data File 8 for 2011 (http://www.eia.gov/cneaf/electricity/page/eia861.html).

[5] Institute for Electric Efficiency, Utility-Scale Smart Meter Deployments, Plans & Proposals (May 2012).

[6] Innovation Electricity Efficiency, Utility-Scale Smart Meter Deployments: A Foundation for Expanded Grid Benefits (August 2013).

Note: Commission staff has not independently verified the accuracy of EIA or IEE data.

(A) Saturation and Penetration Rate of Advanced Meters

Recent data from various sources provide consistent estimates of advanced meter penetration rates. The Energy Information Administration (EIA) reports that in 2011, approximately 37.3 million advanced meters were in use out of 151.7 million meters nationwide, indicating a 24.6 percent penetration rate.[4] The most recent FERC Survey of advanced meters, conducted in 2012 and reported in the 2012 Demand Response and Advanced Metering Report, showed a penetration rate of 22.9 percent.[5] Other sources report similar numbers. For example, data collected by the Institute for Electric Efficiency (IEE) in May 2012 indicate that advanced meters represent approximately 23.5 percent of all meters.[6] More recently, IEE, which has changed its name to Innovation Electricity Efficiency, released an August 2013 report indicating that as of July 2013 almost 46 million smart meters have been installed in the U.S.[7] IEE's recent data implies an advanced meter penetration rate of approximately 30 percent.

Table 1 summarizes the available information on advanced meter installations.

Developments and Issues in Advanced Metering

As indicated above, there has been an increase in the penetration of advanced meters between 2007 and 2013. Federal, state and local governmental entities as well as industry stakeholders continue to develop policies and infrastructure to facilitate deployment of advanced metering and address issues concerning its use. What follows are examples of continued programmatic support for advanced meters, demonstrated benefits of advanced meters, and continued public concerns with deployment of advanced meters.

Federal and State Programmatic Support for Advanced Meters

Support for the deployment of advanced meters continues at the federal and state levels. The American Recovery and Reinvestment Act of 2009 (Recovery Act)[8] appropriated $4.5 billion to the U.S. Department of Energy (DOE) for grid modernization programs, with $3.4 billion of that amount devoted to the Smart Grid Investment Grant (SGIG) program, a public-private partnership initiative for leveraging investments in grid modernization. As of June 30, 2013, approximately 12.8 million advanced meters were installed and operational using Recovery Act funding of the SGIG program.[9] Ultimately, 15.5 million advanced meters are expected to be installed and operational under SGIG. All SGIG projects are expected to reach completion between 2013 and 2014.

Collaborative Industry-Government Efforts

Industry has worked with the National Institute of Standards and Technology (NIST), DOE, state public utility commissions, and organizations such as the North American Energy Standards Board (NAESB) to standardize the types and format of data made available from advanced meters and to use that information to develop new customer services and products. For example, Green Button initiated by NIST, DOE and the White House's Office of Science and Technology Policy (OSTP),[10] is now an industry-led effort to provide electricity customers with secure energy-usage data in a standardized, easy-to-understand format that is accessible from personal computers and mobile devices. A consumer who has a smart meter need only click on a "Green Button" icon at a participating utility's website to download his/her own hourly electricity usage information, typically for up to 13 months.[11] As of May 2013, 27 utilities with operations in 17 states and the District of Columbia have voluntarily committed to participate in the program, and an additional seven utilities have activated programs that allow their customers to securely download their usage data using Green Button.[12] In addition, demand response providers (i.e., curtailment service providers, aggregators or retail customers) can use Green Button data as a verification tool for their demand response programs.[13]

In late 2012, after considerable additional work by utilities and others within the Smart Grid Interoperability Panel (SGIP) framework,[14] SDG&E launched Green Button Connect My Data, which allows customers to automatically send their energy usage data to third-party providers, giving customers additional options to view their previous day's usage data using a smartphone application.[15] In addition, some federal agencies are working to incorporate Green Button data into their programs. For example, the Environmental Protection Agency's (EPA) Home Energy Yardstick tool is now compatible with Green Button data.[16] To help promote the widespread standardization and adoption of Green Button software, NIST established a new Priority Action Plan (PAP) to standardize the testing and certification protocols for utility and vendor Green Button implementations.[17]

The wealth of information produced by advanced meters has spurred the increased development of customer services and products, such as home energy reports, home energy management software, and mobile software applications (*e.g.*, notifications, outage/restoration mapping, usage profiles, billing, and service requests). Certain utilities[18] have partnered with third-party software providers to develop interface applications that simplify and deliver energy consumption data directly to retail customers. For example, monthly energy consumption data reports can alert customers to potential cost-savings from energy efficiency measures, behavioral changes or alternative rate programs.

Demonstrated Benefits of Advanced Meters

Recent storm activity and extreme weather events have provided utilities that have deployed advanced meters with an opportunity to assess the meters' ability to contribute to power system resiliency and help facilitate efficient restoration of electric service following outages caused by storm damage. Electric system outages can be the result of small, medium, and very large scale events spanning several states that often impact other infrastructure systems (*e.g.*, communication, financial, and health care).[19] State regulators and utilities continue to review system hardening and resiliency measures designed to combat and mitigate future storm damage and outages, and the application of new information and communication technologies, including advanced meters, are now a featured component of storm response discussions.[20] Some of the early reports on how advanced meters integrated with other technologies have helped keep the lights on and enabled faster service restorations during recent weather events include the following:

June 2012 "Derecho" and Other Storm Events: During the June 2012 "Derecho" wind storm, advanced meters installed in Atlantic City Electric's New Jersey service territory helped the utility predict the location and extent of the outages, and deploy repair crews to areas where they were most effective.[21] Also in June 2012, Electric Power Board Chattanooga (EPB Chattanooga) employed automated switches working in tandem with advanced meters to reduce the total number of customer power outages by at least half, and avoided 58 million minutes of power disruptions for their customers.[22] EPB Chattanooga was also able to restore power one and a half days sooner than would have been possible prior to the switch and meter upgrades, and the municipality realized $1.4 million in operational savings. Similarly, during a separate storm event in April 2013, Commonwealth Edison reported that the use of automated switches and advanced meters prevented 20,000 service interruptions.[23]

Hurricane Sandy: In October 2012, after the landing of Hurricane Sandy, Baltimore Gas and Electric (BGE) and Pepco noted that advanced meters assisted with efficient storm restoration, as well as customer outreach efforts, in Maryland and the District of Columbia. BGE was able to dispatch crews more efficiently by quickly identifying areas where power was already restored. Both BGE and Pepco noted that potential communication barriers were avoided by using advanced meter signals, instead of calling residential customers to confirm restoration of electric service.24,25

In November 2012, San Diego Gas & Electric (SDG&E) announced plans to integrate advanced meters with an advanced Outage Management System to track multiple outages during large storms and to better organize planned outages.[26] This will allow SDG&E to reach an outage site prior to customer calls and better manage and monitor power flow and undertake planned outages.[27]

Privacy and Other Customer Concerns

New and emerging technologies can modernize the electric grid, while also providing customers with new tools that engage and meet customer needs. However, concerns about the security and privacy of customer data remain. To this end, policy makers and industry continue to work through NIST and other forums to develop privacy policies and procedures.[28]

Interval usage data from advanced meters in conjunction with other enabling technologies can expand opportunities for demand response and energy efficiency programs. Facilitated by the DOE and the EPA, the State & Local Energy Efficiency Action Network (SEE Action) issued an analysis of state approaches to data access, security and privacy when utilities provide customer data to a third party for energy efficiency programs. California, Colorado, Oklahoma, Oregon, Texas, Vermont, Washington, and Wisconsin have adopted rules governing third-party access to customer data, and seven state commissions have open dockets as of December 2012.[29] The National Association of Regulatory Utility Commissioners (NARUC) released an updated primer concerning, in part, the security of data. The primer addresses cybersecurity for the electric grid and provides conceptual cybersecurity basics, the jurisdictional landscape, and best-practices for policymakers' consideration.[30]

To address customer issues with deployment of advanced meters, states continue to develop "opt-out policies", which may include a fee for customers who object to the installation of an advanced meter to actually "opt-out" of having the meter installed. Many utilities have argued that opt-out fees are justified due to costs associated with having a mix of traditional and advanced meters on a utility's system. For example, the Nevada Public Utility Commission ruled in January 2013 that NV Energy may charge opt-out fees for a trial period.[31] The Michigan Public Service Commission also allowed opt-out fees in a May 2013 order approving a Detroit Edison advanced metering residential opt-out program.[32] In contrast to the above, New Hampshire enacted legislation in June 2012 prohibiting electric utilities from installing and maintaining advanced meter gateway devices without the property owner's consent, thereby establishing an opt-in approach for the state.[33]

An Illinois nonprofit consumer advocacy group sued the City of Naperville to prevent advanced meters from being installed due to concerns over privacy, property rights and the health effects of radio frequency waves associated with the meters' wireless technology. However, the U.S. District Court dismissed the complaint, finding that the factual evidence presented on the health effects of radio frequencies was not sufficient to justify cancelling the City of Naperville's advanced metering rollout. The court also found that the City of Naperville's privacy protections—including anonymous customer ID numbers, data aggregation, and a customer bill of rights[34]—were not proven insufficient to protect customers' right to privacy.[35]

Other State Legislative and Regulatory Activity

- **California.** In October 2012, the California Public Utilities Commission (CPUC) directed the state's investor-owned utilities to ensure interoperability between in-home energy monitoring devices and their advanced meters. In conjunction, the CPUC directed the state's largest utilities to facilitate a competitive, third-party retail market where customers can select from a variety of in-home energy management devices capable of communicating utility-sponsored energy conservation measures and enabling consumers to respond to demand response events.[36]
- **Connecticut.** In February 2013, the Connecticut Department of Energy and Environmental Protection (DEEP) issued the first Comprehensive Energy Strategy for the state as required by Public Act 11-80. Advanced metering technology, facilitated by dynamic pricing policies, is a central component of the report's multi-pronged strategy for achieving sustainable, day-to-day reductions of peak electricity demand.[37]
- **Illinois.** In June 2013, the Illinois Commerce Commission (ICC) approved updated cost-recovery rates for ComEd and Ameren Illinois in conjunction with the advanced meter deployment required by the Energy Infrastructure and Modernization Act (EIMA).[38,39] The ICC action is in response to the May 2013 enactment of Illinois Senate Bill 9,[40] which amended the EIMA[41] to include cost-recovery rates for the law's mandated advanced meter rollout.[42]
- **Kentucky.** In October 2012, the Kentucky Public Service Commission (KPSC) initiated an administrative proceeding to consider the implementation of advanced metering infrastructure (AMI) technologies and time-of-use electricity prices.[43] The

proceedings investigate implementation costs, interoperability standards, and societal impacts related to recommendations made in the state's *Smart Grid Roadmap Initiative* issued in June 2012.[44] The KPSC, in collaboration with a consortium of state utilities, is examining various smart grid technologies and pricing structures that encourage greater energy efficiency.[45] In May 2013, the ongoing Joint Parties Collaborative proposed to issue a report on utility industry recommendations by June 2014.[46]

- **Maine**. By the end of 2012, the Central Maine Power Company, Bangor Hydroelectric, and the Maine Public Service Company had almost completed installation of advanced metering devices, as well as associated communication and data management systems.[47] Concomitant with near full advanced meter deployment, the Maine Public Utilities Commission approved plans for the Central Maine Power Company to initiate a time-ofuse pricing program for residential and small commercial customers.[48]
- **Pennsylvania.** In December 2012, the Pennsylvania Public Utility Commission (PAPUC) issued a final order requiring electric utilities to establish a standard electronic format for providing consenting customers and third-parties with direct access to customer data. The PAPUC established the Electric Data Exchange Working Group, comprised of utilities and stakeholders, to oversee development of standards for acquiring interval usage data via a secure web portal. The Working Group is expected to reach consensus on standards for "bill quality" interval data by March 2015.[49] In December 2012, the Metropolitan Edison Company, Pennsylvania Electric Company, Pennsylvania Power Company, and West Penn Power Company submitted their advanced meter deployment plans for approval to the PAPUC,[50] as required by Act 129.[51] Beginning in January 2013, the companies expect to install approximately 98.5 percent of all advanced metering devices by 2019.[52] In January 2013, PECO Energy Company submitted its Phase II Smart Meter Implementation Plan to the PAPUC. PECO expects to have 600,000 advanced metering devices installed by June 2013, with 1.2 million devices installed before 2015 and full deployment achieved by 2019.[53]

(B) Existing Demand Response Programs and Time-Based Rate Programs

Commission staff surveyed existing demand response and time-based rate programs in 2012 (see 2012 FERC Demand Response and Advanced Metering Report) and intends to conduct another survey during 2014. In addition, the U.S. Energy Information Administration (EIA) collects specific data for demand-side management programs designed to modify patterns of electricity usage, including the timing and level of electric demand.[54] EIA expects to release 2012 data in October 2013.[55]

In March 2013, NERC released initial Demand Response Availability Data System (DADS) data results through the 2011-2012 winter (October 2, 2011 to March 31, 2012) periods.[56] NERC states that 80 entities reported demand response program data for the 2011 summer reporting period and 74 entities reported for the 2011-2012 winter reporting period. Aggregate data is presented for reporting entities operating in both the U.S. and Canada, and NERC states the total number of reporting entities may grow to over 200 with the completion of subsequent phases of DADS that are designed to include reliability programs and data on economic demand response and time-based pricing programs.[57]

(C) Annual Resource Contribution of Demand Resources

The FERC survey of demand resources is undertaken on a biennial basis, as noted above. As a result, Table 2 compares the survey data for calendar year 2011 as reported in the 2012 Demand Response and Advanced Metering Report to separate values for 2012 from Regional Transmission Organization (RTO) and Independent System Operator (ISO) information sources.[58] Based on publicly available sources of information, the potential resource contribution by demand response in U.S. RTO/ISO markets increased by 6.3 percent from 2010 to 2011 to 32,488 MW, but fell in 2012 to 28,303 MW, a year-on-year decrease of 12.9 percent. As a percentage of peak load, demand response potential decreased by 0.7 percentage points from 2011 to 2012. Overall, the demand response resources' potential contribution in U.S. RTO/ISO markets has increased by 4.1 percent since 2009.[59]

Table 2. Demand Response Resource Potential at U.S. ISOs and RTOs

RTO/ISO	2011 Demand Response (MW)	2011 Percent of Peak Demand[9]	2012 Demand Response (MW)	2012 Percent of Peak Demand[9]
California ISO (CAISO)	2,270 [1]	5.0%	2,430 [1]	5.2%
Electric Reliability Council of Texas (ERCOT)	1,570 [2]	2.3%	1,750 [3]	2.6%
ISO New England, Inc. (ISO-NE)	1,231 [2]	4.4%	2,769 [4]	10.7%
Midcontinent Independent System Operator (MISO)	9,529 [2]	9.2%	7,197 [5]	7.3%
New York Independent System Operator (NYISO)	2,247 [2]	6.6%	1,888 [6]	5.8%
PJM Interconnection, LLC (PJM)	14,127 [2]	8.9%	10,825 [7]	7.0%
Southwest Power Pool, Inc. (SPP)	1,514 [2]	3.2%	1,444 [8]	3.1%
Total RTO/ISO	**32,488**	**6.7%**	**28,303**	**6.0%**

Sources:

[1] California ISO 2012 Annual Report on Market Issues and Performance.

[2] 2012 Assessment of Demand Response and Advanced Metering, FERC Staff Report.

[3] ERCOT Quick Facts (May 2013).

[4] 2012 Assessment of the ISO New England Electric Markets, Potomac Economics.

[5] 2012 State of the Market Report for the MISO Electric Markets, Potomac Economics.

[6] 2012 State of the Market Report for the New York ISO Markets, Potomac Economics.

[7] PJM Load Response Activity Report, July 2012, "Delivery Year 2012-2013 Active Participants in PJM Load Response Program".

[8] SPP Fast Facts (March 1, 2013).

[9] Estimates based on peak demand data from the following: California ISO 2012 Annual Report on Market Issues and Performance; ERCOT 2011 & 2012 State of the Market Reports; 2011 Assessment of the ISO New England Electricity Markets; ISO-NE Net Energy and Peak Load Report (April 2013); 2011 & 2012 State of the Market Reports for the MISO Electricity Markets; 2011 & 2012 State of the Market Reports for the New York ISO Markets; 2011 & 2012 PJM State of the Markets Reports, Vol. 2; SPP 2011 & 2012 State of the Market Reports.

Recognizing that separate data sets are utilized for 2011 and 2012 in Table 2, general results indicate that CAISO, ERCOT, ISO-NE realized increases in demand response, while other RTO markets realized declines. Significant decreases in demand response potential[60] were realized in the PJM markets. According to the market monitor's report for the 2012/2013 delivery year, a marked decrease in clearing prices in PJM's forward capacity auction caused the number of credits for demand response to fall sharply in 2012.[61] The market monitor also concluded that the decrease in demand response potential was influenced by the discontinuation of the Interruptible Load for Reliability program after the 2011/2012 planning year. The decrease in registrations in PJM's load management programs was partially offset by an increase in registrations under its economic programs.

Summer 2013 Demand Response Deployments

Demand response resources made significant contributions to balancing supply and demand for several RTOs and ISOs in the summer of 2013. A heat wave in the Eastern United States during the third week of July and in mid-September drove demand for electricity to record levels in some areas.

On July 19, NYISO set a new record for peak demand of 33,955 MW.[62] NYISO activated demand response resources statewide on July 18 and 19, as well as deploying these resources every day throughout the week to relieve historically congested areas of the lower Hudson Valley and southeastern New York.[63] NYISO states it successfully met this record demand through strong performances by demand response, generation and transmission resources, coordination between NYISO and its neighboring regions, and high availability of wind resources.[64]

The high temperatures also resulted in deployment of demand response in PJM. On three days beginning July 15, PJM called long lead time emergency demand response resources for several of its zones. PJM dispatched 652 MW of demand response resources for two consecutive days on July 15 and 16, and dispatched 1,638 MW of demand response resources on July 18. Economic demand response also contributed to the PJM system during the week. The estimated hourly economic demand response reached levels of approximately 250 MW, 400 MW, 870 MW, 630 MW and 625 MW on each day, respectively, from July 15 through July 19.[65] The combination of emergency and economic demand response resources, in addition to other measures, helped PJM address the transmission constraints, high loads, and unplanned generation outages experienced during the week of July 15, 2013.[66]

On September 11, 2013 PJM called on and received approximately 5,949 MW of demand response resources, which represented the largest amount of demand response PJM has ever received. This demand response helped address the imbalance between supply and demand caused by unusually hot weather and local equipment problems which created emergency conditions in four states. Consumer demand for electricity reached a record-setting 144,370 MW on September 10 while, thanks in part to demand response resources, on September 11 the demand on PJM's system was down to 142,071 MW. The September 10 and 11 peak demands reached 90 percent of PJM's past July 18 summer peak demand of 157,509 MW. While PJM was forced to direct local utilities to curtail 150 MW to ensure reliability, PJM credited voluntary demand response resources with playing a vital role in keeping the power grid stable and air conditioners running during the September peaks.[67]

In ISO-NE, demand peaked at 27,359 MW in the late afternoon of July 19. ISO-NE dispatched approximately 200 MW of emergency demand resources that day in response to high temperatures, unexpectedly high demand and unit outages. On July 15 and 18, wholesale prices rose past $200 per MWh, and exceeded $400 per MWh on July 19.[68] In addition to dispatching demand response resources, ISO-NE also made two requests to retail consumers to conserve electricity voluntarily.[69]

In CAISO, high temperatures in early July led CAISO to issue calls for consumers in the northern half of the state to voluntarily reduce their electricity use on July 1-2.[70] Although forecast to hit an all-time high on July 1, peak demand came in significantly under the forecast, which CAISO attributed to the impact of demand response programs and voluntary conservation.[71]

California Activities

The CAISO hosted a workshop on May 13, 2013,[72] and later released a whitepaper titled "California ISO Demand Response and Energy Efficiency Roadmap: Making the Most of Green Grid Resources."[73] The demand response and energy efficiency roadmap comprises four parallel and roughly concurrent paths or tracks of activity that run from 2013 through 2020.[74] The four paths are: the load reshaping path; the resource sufficiency path; the operations path; and the monitoring path. The roadmap highlights the need for inter-agency coordination and specific areas where coordination and communication are necessary to build new market opportunities for demand response and energy efficiency solutions.[75]

On June 17, 2013, the California Energy Commission (CEC) conducted a workshop to gather input on public policies needed to expand the amount of automated demand response resources available to CAISO.[76] At the CEC workshop, the CAISO indicated that the expected increase in solar and wind integration will alter the daytime load profile in the CAISO system as early as 2015. CAISO expects the system will experience a deep daytime load trough with a rapid and significant escalation between 4 p.m. to 8 p.m. CAISO suggested that flexible demand response resources may be needed to address these unpredictable situations.[77]

ERCOT Activities

ERCOT launched two new demand response programs aimed at improving the reserve margin during summer peak events. The first program, launched in June 2012 and expanded in December 2012, is the 30-minute Emergency Response Service (ERS) program.[78] This pilot project will allow eligible participants a half hour to respond to ERCOT requests to reduce their electricity use, and is open to individual customers or an aggregated group of consumers who can reduce demand on the ERCOT grid by at least 100 kilowatts.[79] The board authorized ERCOT to procure up to a total of 150 MW for the pilot.

The second pilot, launched in March 2013, is the Weather-Sensitive Emergency Response Service pilot.[80] This pilot is open to electricity customers that can reduce power use by at least 100 kilowatts. Through qualified scheduling entities, participants will be paid based on how much they reduce demand, either in testing or during an actual event.[81] ERCOT can call on resources beginning with the first level of energy emergency alert (EEA 1), when operating reserves drop below 2,300 MW. Most ERCOT demand response programs go into effect during EEA 2 when reserves drop below 1,750 MW.

NERC's Demand Response Availability Data System

In March 2013 NERC published early stage DADS results for two time periods: the 2011 summer (April 1, 2011 to September 30, 2011) and the 2011-2012 winter (October 2, 2011 to March 31, 2012) periods.[82] For the U.S. and Canadian entities providing information about demand response programs that are deployed for reliability purposes, NERC reports there were 527 demand response deployments during the summer of 2011. The average number of demand response resources enrolled during the 2011 summer months was 6.46 million resources, on average the combined capacity of these resources was 50,919 MW, and the average sustained response period was 3 hours and 6 minutes.[83] The average number of demand response resources enrolled during the 2011-2012 winter period was 5.34 million resources, on average the combined capacity of these resources was 48,686 MW, and the average sustained response period was 1 hours and 43 minutes.[84]

(D) Potential for Demand Response As a Quantifiable, Reliable Resource for Regional Planning Purposes

The Commission continues to ensure that demand resources are provided comparable treatment in jurisdictional transmission planning processes, processing compliance filings in response to Order No. 1000, which reaffirmed Order No. 890's requirement that public utility transmission providers consider all types of resources, including demand response and energy efficiency, on a comparable basis in transmission planning.[85]

As part of the Recovery Act, the DOE awarded funds for collaborative transmission planning efforts in the Western, Eastern and Texas Interconnections, and these efforts are taking demand response into account.[86] Transmission planning studies in the Western, Eastern and Texas Interconnections are conducted by the Western Electricity Coordinating Council (WECC), the Eastern Interconnection Planning Collaborative (EIPC), and the Electric Reliability Council of Texas (ERCOT), respectively. WECC,[87] EIPC,[88] and ERCOT[89] have each undertaken collaborative work efforts that develop long-term electricity supply futures, estimate the associated transmission requirements, and prepare long-term interconnection-wide transmission plans.[90] Smart grid technologies and demand resources are considered as components within a broad range of alternative supply futures.

For example, demand response study case inputs are to be analyzed in WECC's 20-year plan,[91] and the Western Interconnection SPSC has approved the formation of a task force to examine using demand response for integrating variable generation in the West.[92]

In the Eastern Interconnection, NARUC and the Eastern Interconnection States' Planning Council funded an assessment of demand-side resources and their existing and forecasted deployments within the eastern United States.[93] Additionally, the Oak Ridge National Laboratory (ORNL), working in part with the EIPC Stakeholder Steering Committee, modified and updated the Commission's National Assessment of Demand Response (NADR) model to forecast system peak demand by state and census division.[94]

ERCOT, with the assistance of stakeholders, developed a set of three scenarios for use in the long term study of the Texas Interconnection. All three scenarios consider and model demand response resources.[95] One of the three scenarios includes a sensitivity analysis that assumes a technology-specific mandate to expand demand response.[96]

(E) Steps Taken to Ensure That, in Regional Transmission Planning and Operations, Demand Resources Are Provided Equitable Treatment As a Quantifiable, Reliable Resource Relative to the Resource Obligations of Any Load-Serving Entity, Transmission Provider, or Transmitting Party

As part of its ongoing effort to remove barriers to entry and ensure a level playing field for all resources that are technically capable of providing a service to have access to wholesale and interstate markets, the Commission has taken a number of actions related to demand response. This section summarizes those actions taken in the past year, other actions taken at the federal level, and recent state and industry actions taken at the retail level on demand response programs.

FERC Demand Response Orders and Activities

Order No. 745

In March 2011, the Commission issued Order No. 745 relating to demand response compensation in organized wholesale energy markets.[97] The Commission has accepted filings that PJM and ISO-NE submitted in order to comply with the requirements of the rule.[98] Both MISO and CAISO have filed multiple compliance filings, and the Commission has largely accepted their proposals, establishing limited requirements for further tariff revisions.[99] The Commission issued an initial order on NYISO's Order No. 745 compliance filing in May 2013, requiring NYISO to make further tariff revisions.[100] Rehearing of that order is currently pending before the Commission. Additionally, on August 14, 2013, NYISO submitted a second compliance filing, which is pending before the Commission. SPP also has an Order No. 745 compliance filing before the Commission. The Commission rejected in part SPP's initial compliance filing and required more explanation on the remainder of that filing.[101] In May 2012, SPP submitted a second compliance filing, which is currently pending before the Commission. In January 2013, SPP replied to a request for additional information from Commission staff relating to certain aspects of its second compliance filing.

Order No. 1000

As noted above, Order No. 1000, issued in July 2011, reaffirmed Order No. 890's requirement that public utility transmission providers consider all types of resources, including demand response and energy efficiency, on a comparable basis in transmission planning.[102] In the first half of 2013, the Commission issued 15 orders in response to compliance filings addressing the regional transmission planning and cost allocation requirements of Order No. 1000, addressing each transmission planning region's compliance proposals and directing further compliance filings. Currently, the Commission is in the process of receiving further compliance filings, and in some cases rehearing requests, with respect to each of the transmission planning regions. Moreover, the Commission has started to receive separate filings that include proposals for compliance with the interregional requirements of Order No. 1000.

NAESB Demand Response and Energy Efficiency M&V Standards

In February 2013, the Commission issued a final rule (Order No. 676-G) amending its regulations to incorporate by reference NAESB's business practice standards on the measurement and verification of demand response and energy efficiency resources that participate in organized wholesale electricity markets.[103] The NAESB demand response measurement and verification (M&V) standards revised existing NAESB standards by adding specificity to the existing standards in several areas, including meter data reporting, advanced notification, telemetry and meter accuracy. The Final Rule concluded that these revisions to the NAESB demand response M&V standards represented an incremental improvement to the business practices for measuring and verifying demand resource products and services in the organized wholesale electric markets.

The new NAESB M&V standards for energy efficiency provide criteria that will support the measurement and verification of energy efficiency products and services in organized wholesale electric markets. These new standards include four acceptable measurement and verification methodologies that energy efficiency resource providers may use to participate in organized wholesale electricity markets. They also provide criteria for determining which type of baseline to use in various situations, such as the installation of new energy efficient equipment and processes or the replacement of outdated equipment. The standards also contain rules regarding statistical methods used to accurately determine reduction values, specifications for equipment used to perform measurements, and data validation. The Final Rule concluded that these standards will reduce transaction costs and provide an additional opportunity and increased incentive for energy efficiency resources to participate in the wholesale markets established in RTO and ISO regions.

Other Federal Demand Response Activities

National Forum on Demand Response

As part of the Implementation Proposal for the National Action Plan on Demand Response,[104] the U.S. Department of Energy (DOE) and FERC sponsored a National Forum on Demand Response. Within the National Forum, DOE and FERC staff worked with state officials, demand response industry representatives, members of a National Action Plan Coalition, and experts from research organizations to share ideas, examine barriers and explore solutions for advancing demand response. To help answer questions of what remains to be done with demand response, working groups were formed to focus on key demand response technical, programmatic and policy issues. DOE funding supported the efforts in all four areas.

In February 2013, DOE and FERC staff released a series of new reports prepared by National Forum working groups created to address four issues:[105]

- Cost effectiveness
- Measurement and verification
- Program design and implementation
- Tools and methods

DOE Smart Grid Investment Grants

A series of Department of Energy (DOE) reports released in December 2012 confirm the operational and customer service benefits of AMI in select SGIG projects. The DOE's Office of Electricity Deliverability and Energy Reliability reviewed SGIG projects at or near completing AMI integration with: 1) enterprise software (15 of 63 projects),[106] 2) automated capacitor banks (eight of 26 projects),[107] and 3) automated feeder switching (four of 42 projects).[108] Of the 15 SGIG projects with AMI-enterprise software integration reviewed, representing approximately 3.5 million advanced meters, all showed lower meter operation costs, primarily due to reduced labor and vehicle costs related to remote meter reading and automated billing services. Projects with lower customer densities per distribution line-mile observed the largest savings per customer served. Of the eight SGIG projects with automated AMI-capacitor bank integration, initial results indicate the potential of between 1 and 2.5 percent reductions in peak demand. Of the four SGIG projects with automated AMI-feeder switching, all showed a reduction in both the frequency of outages and in the amount of time customers were without power.

DOE Smart Grid Demonstrations

The Smart Grid Demonstration Program (SGDP), operated by DOE, includes nine projects that employ demand response technologies or otherwise enhance demand response.[109] One SGDP project, the Battelle Memorial Institute's Pacific Northwest project, which is being undertaken by in five states by 12 utilities with more than 60,000 customers, is in part using new technologies to provide two-way communication between distributed generation, storage, and demand response assets. A second SGDP project, the National Rural Electric Cooperative Association's (NRECA) Enhanced Demand and Distribution Management Regional Demonstration project is implementing new technologies at 27 cooperatives in 11 states with different geographies and climates. The NRECA project will conduct studies in advanced volt/volt-ampere reactive power for total demand, demand response, critical peak pricing, water heater and air conditioning load control, thermal storage, energy usage portal pilots, and consumer in-home energy display pilots. A third SGDP project, NSTAR Electric and Gas Corporation's Automated Meter Reading-Based Dynamic Pricing, will enable residential dynamic pricing [time-of-use (TOU), critical peak rates, and peak time rebates] and two-way direct load control by capturing automated meter reading (AMR) data transmissions and communicating through existing customer-sited broadband connections in conjunction with home area networks.

Wholesale Demand Response Communication Protocols

The Smart Grid Interoperability Panel[110] formed a Priority Action Plan (PAP) 19 working group to develop and enhance data exchange between RTOs and demand response aggregators. The PAP 19 working group completed work on the Wholesale Demand Response Communication Protocol (WDRCP) on September 21, 2012.[111] The WDRCP defines use cases and creates model extensions for the modeling of distributed demand resources,[112] as well as ways to deploy, measure, and evaluate distributed demand resources in wholesale markets. One of the key features of the WDRCP is the direct use of the Requirement Specification for Wholesale Standard DR Signals (published by NAESB) and the International Electrotechnical Commission's (IEC) Common Information Model, a set of standards widely used by utilities and transmission organizations around the world, including North American RTOs/ISOs.

A working group within the IEC's Technical Committee 57, Power System Communications, is considering the WDRCP for possible incorporation into the Common Information Model standards. The WDRCP protocol has been mapped to two leading demand response standards/applications, namely Open Automated Demand Response (OpenADR), a system for utility and third party communications with building automation systems in commercial and industrial buildings, and MultiSpeak, a system of standardized terminology and data objects used in systems integration for smaller utility operations, including many electric cooperatives.

DOD & GSA Federal Efforts

Managing more than 300,000 buildings on some 500 installations, including barracks, data centers, office buildings and hospitals,[113] the Department of Defense (DOD) is the single largest energy consumer in the Nation.[114] Because of its size, the DOD recognizes it can use its own facilities to overcome development and deployment barriers for promising technologies, including demand response and advanced metering infrastructure.[115] DOD environmental research programs foster technological innovations, assist in developing technologies, and accelerate cost-effective technology transitions into commercial markets through collaborative efforts among federal agencies, academia and industry. For example, DOD is demonstrating enhanced demand response program participation for Naval District Washington (NDW), the regional provider of common operating support to Naval installations within a 100-mile radius of the Pentagon. NDW installations encompass more than 4,000 square miles in portions of Maryland, Virginia and the District of

Columbia.[116] NDW has invested in advanced meters and meter data systems, and, as a part of its overall energy reduction strategy, plans to integrate its energy management systems and tools to demonstrate the ability to cost-effectively and securely participate in demand response programs.[117] The NDW project will also determine how to transfer the technology and processes to other DOD services.

The U.S. General Services Administration (GSA) owns and leases over 354 million square feet in 9,600 federal buildings,[118] and more than 30 federal agencies depend on the GSA's Energy Division to assist with energy procurement.[119] In 2012, the GSA Energy Division assisted with two separate wholesale demand response transactions for approximately "24 MW of demand response (~8 MW annually over a three year term)" for U.S. Department of Veterans Affairs facilities in NYISO and GSA facilities in PJM.[120]

Other State Legislative and Regulatory Activities Related to Demand Response

This section highlights several developments in retail demand response and time-based pricing activities since the publication of the previous report. In most cases, the developments reviewed for this report point to a continued expansion of demand response programs at the retail level, including, in some cases, an evolution of recent time-based pricing pilots into full program offerings.

- **Arkansas.** Act 1078 (Regulation of Electric Demand Response Act), approved on April 11, 2013, specifies the authority possessed by the Arkansas Public Service Commission (APSC) to establish the terms and conditions for marketing and selling demand response to retail customers or into wholesale electricity markets. The latter is prohibited unless the APSC determines that doing so is in the public interest. The marketing and selling of demand response by a municipal electric utility or a consolidated municipal utility improvement district is regulated by the local governing body rather than the APSC.[121]
- **California.** There have been several developments related to demand response in California over the past year. As previously noted, the CEC conducted a workshop on June 17, 2013 to gather input on

public policies needed to expand the amount of automated demand response resources available to CAISO.[122] Prior to the CEC workshop and in a November 29, 2012 decision, the California Public Utilities Commission (CPUC) resolved certain policy issues related to its proposed Electric Rule No. 24, allowing retail customers to bid demand response resources, on their own or through an aggregator, directly into CAISO's wholesale energy markets.[123]

The CPUC also issued Decision 12-04-045 on April 30, 2012, directing the state's Demand Response Measurement and Evaluation Committee (DRMEC)[124] to submit a detailed process evaluation plan that lists all demand response programs to be evaluated during 2012-2014, along with an explanation of the necessity of each evaluation.[125] The DRMEC is required to conduct annual statewide studies assessing the load impacts of demand response programs, but no guidance was provided on process evaluations— which assess how effectively programs are designed and delivered—until the issuance of Decision 12-04-045. The process evaluation studies will be available for review by Fall 2014.[126]

In addition, prior to the announced retirement of Southern California Edison's (SCE) San Onofre Nuclear Generating Station (SONGS),[127] the CPUC issued Decision 13-04-017 on April 18, 2013 approving San Diego Gas & Electric's (SDG&E) and SCE's proposed revisions to their existing demand response programs to mitigate the effects of the continuing outage of SONGS Units 2 and 3.[128] Changes to SCE's programs are estimated to amount to an additional 58 MW of load reduction; the incremental impact of changes to SDG&E's programs was not specified.

In May 2012, the CEC approved the latest version of its Title 24 Building Energy Efficiency Standards, which include requirements for automated demand response controls in certain new buildings. The standards are to take effect on January 1, 2014.[129] As defined in Title 24, "demand responsive controls" allow lighting levels in buildings to be automatically reduced in response to a demand response signal from a local utility. The revisions to Title 24 specify that the lighting controls must be able to receive and respond to "at least one standards based messaging protocol."[130]

- **Connecticut.** In its Comprehensive Energy Strategy, released earlier this year, the Connecticut Department of Energy & Environmental Protection (DEEP) recommended "increased participation in [demand response] programs to help control the costs for Connecticut ratepayers and to allow ISO New England greater flexibility in managing the [wholesale electricity] system."[131] Specifically, the strategy recommended that, in addition to increasing the penetration of advanced meters, the state expand time-of-use pricing and other dynamic rate mechanisms to provide customers with financial incentives to shift their electricity use to lower-price periods.

- **Georgia.** Georgia Power has put in place a time-of-use rate specifically for homes with plug-in electric vehicles. The rate is structured with on-peak, off-peak and "super off-peak" times; the latter provides a significant discount over peak hours during the summer season, and a smaller discount during the rest of the year.[132]
- **Idaho.** Based on the results of its 2013 Integrated Resource Plan, which estimated no peak hour capacity shortages until 2016, Idaho Power filed a petition with the Idaho Public Utilities Commission (IPUC) to temporarily suspend two of its demand response programs. The IPUC approved a settlement stipulation to the petition, which specifies that existing customers will receive a "continuity payment" to encourage them to remain enrolled in the two suspended programs and that no new customers will be enrolled while the suspensions are in effect. The status of the suspended programs will be reconsidered ahead of the 2014 summer season.[133]
- **Illinois.** The Energy Infrastructure Modernization Act requires participating utilities to file proposed tariffs offering optional peak-time rebate programs to their residential customers within 60 days after approval of the utilities' advanced metering plans by the Illinois Commerce Commission (ICC).[134] In a February 2013 Interim Order, the ICC approved ComEd's proposed Peak Time Rebate (PTR) program, conditioned on the utility making slight amendments to the program plan. The Order notes that the PTR program's first curtailment will take place after June 1, 2015.[135] Because Ameren Illinois does not yet have a Commission-approved AMI plan, it does not have a statutory obligation to file a PTR tariff at this time.[136]
- **Maine.** The Maine Public Utilities Commission (MPUC) approved a time-of-use rate for Central Maine Power Company (CMP) for the one-year period beginning March 1, 2013. The optional program is available to residential and small commercial customers, and is delivered by NB Power, which services approximately one-third of CMP's residential and small commercial load.[137] In addition, the

MPUC approved the establishment of a pilot program to test the ability of cost-effective "non-transmission alternatives," such as distributed generation, energy efficiency and demand response, to defer or eliminate the need for new transmission while meeting reliability requirements. In its 2012 Annual Report, the Efficiency Maine Trust, the statewide energy efficiency program administrator, noted that the pilot is scheduled to issue a request for proposals for non-transmission alternative resources in September 2013, and that resources are expected to be in operation by July 1, 2014.[138]

- **Maryland**. Baltimore Gas and Electric (BGE) and Delmarva Power and Light (DP&L) both have peak time rebate programs in place that provide a credit for reductions in electricity consumption during critical peak events. This dynamic rate structure is applicable to BGE's residential customers and to DP&L's residential and small commercial customers.[139] In its June 2012 Request for Authorization, Southern Maryland Electric Cooperative (SMECO) suggested that it would offer a time-of-use rate once its advanced meter installation is approved.[140] Utilities in Maryland have a goal of delivering 200 MW of demand response from dynamic pricing programs, in addition to approximately 700 MW from direct load control programs.[141]
  Another factor potentially affecting demand response in the state is the status of the EmPOWER Maryland program. In its recent final report to the state Senate Finance and House Economic Matters Committees about the future of the program,[142] the Maryland Energy Administration (MEA) noted, based on data about the performance of retail demand response programs,[143] that the state is expected to exceed its target of a 15% reduction in per capita peak demand by 2015. MEA recommended that Maryland continue the EmPOWER program, with several significant changes to its structure and energy and demand savings targets. According to MEA, legislation to extend the EmPOWER program is expected to be introduced in 2014.[144]
- **Minnesota**. In November 2012, the Minnesota Public Utilities Commission (MPUC) approved Dakota Electric Association's[145] petition to implement a pilot time-of-use rate for residential electric vehicle charging. The proposed rate is intended to incent customers to charge their electric vehicles during off-peak hours.[146] Also in November 2012, the MPUC approved Minnesota Power's petition to implement a residential timeof-day rate pilot. The pilot incorporates mechanisms for providing customers with feedback about their energy

consumption at two time scales and also defines critical peak pricing periods. It is part of the utility's broader Smart Grid Advanced Metering Infrastructure Pilot Project partially funded by the U.S. Department of Energy.[147]

- **New York**. In December 2012, Consolidated Edison of New York (ConEd) filed a petition seeking approval of changes to its existing demand response programs. Among other things, the utility sought to replace existing communicating thermostats in homes participating in its direct load control program with new wi-fi enabled communicating thermostats, and to increase the program budget to cover the cost of these installations over a five-year period. In addition, ConEd sought to expand the program by offering new participants a plug-in smart outlet to enable remote customer control of temperature settings.[148] In an April 2013 order, the New York Public Service Commission (NYPSC) approved ConEd's proposed program changes with significant changes. Instead of a wholesale replacement of existing communicating thermostats, the utility is allowed to replace thermostats with new wi-fi enabled versions only upon failure of the existing technology; the associated increase in budget was denied. The NYPSC found that the incorporation of the plug-in outlet technology into the direct load control program was premature. It ordered ConEd to continue refining the technology offering for another two years within its current pilot format.[149]
- **Ohio.** Duke Energy Ohio and AEP Ohio are offering new time-of-use rates to their residential customers. At the end of 2012, Duke Energy Ohio submitted an application for a new pilot time-of-use rate, which the Public Utilities Commission of Ohio approved on February 13, 2013.[150] The pilot will target up to 5,000 homes with an advanced meter installed and that meet certain conditions of baseline consumption.[151] Customers electing to participate have a choice of three-hour blocks on summer and winter weekdays from which to select their preferred on-peak period.[152] AEP Ohio is offering two new time-ofuse rates for customers living in its gridSMART Demonstration Project:[153] the "SMART Shift" program offers a single on-peak and off-peak period, while the "SMART Shift Plus" rate incorporates time-of-use and critical peak pricing elements.[154]
- **Pennsylvania.** Under Act 129 of 2008, the Pennsylvania Public Utility Commission (PAPUC) was charged with establishing a state-wide energy efficiency and conservation (EE&C) program. Phase I of

the program (2010-13) set a cumulative energy savings target of three percent of weather-adjusted sales, and a peak demand reduction target of 4.5 percent of each utility's 100 highest demand hours.[155] Phase II of the EE&C program established additional cumulative energy savings targets, but not demand reduction targets, because an assessment of the cost-effectiveness of demand response programs was not available at the time the Implementation Order was issued.[156] In May 2013, the Statewide Evaluator released its demand response study, as directed by the PAPUC. The study found that demand response programs were not cost-effective in 2012, due in part to "aggressive reduction targets" and to the stipulation that utilities reduce peak demand during the 100 hours of highest annual demand, which are difficult to predict. The Statewide Evaluator recommended several changes to the Act 129 demand response requirements and program evaluation for potential inclusion in Phase III of the EE&C program, which would begin in June 2016.[157]

Utilities continue to expand their time-of-use rate offerings for some customers. A timeof-day rate ("hourly pricing") is the default service for large commercial and industrial customers in Pennsylvania, and is an option for medium C&I customers that have an advanced meter installed.[158] On June 1, 2015, medium C&I customers with the appropriate meter will also default to hourly pricing service.[159]

- **Rhode Island.** In a February 2012 order, the Rhode Island Public Utilities Commission (RIPUC) approved a National Grid proposal to conduct a "Load Curtailment Pilot" in the Tiverton/Little Compton area from 2012 - 2017.[160] According to National Grid's revised 2012 System Reliability Procurement Plan, the pilot will test whether demand response can manage local distribution capacity requirements during peak periods.[161] The pilot thus fulfills a requirement under the state's revised System Reliability Procurement Standards to identify "potential non-wire alternative solutions that reduce, avoid, or defer" traditional transmission and distribution solutions.[162] Over the course of the pilot, National Grid plans to install wi-fi programmable controllable thermostats and lighting with enhanced demand response ballasts, as well as some direct load control appliance measures in future years.[163]

  In its 2013 System Reliability Procurement Report, National Grid sought approval to enhance the Load Curtailment Pilot by offering higher energy efficiency incentives, providing additional energy efficiency measures that would not otherwise have been offered through statewide programs, and increasing marketing and participation in the pilot. National Grid estimates that the pilot will deliver annual summer demand savings of 161 kW (1,914 kW lifetime) from the residential and C&I sectors, along with annual energy savings of 500 MWh (5,512 MWh lifetime).[164] The RIPUC approved the continuation of the pilot and the proposed changes to marketing, participation and technology updates.[165]

Industry Demand Response Actions

Leadership in Energy and Environmental Design (LEED)

As part of the Leadership in Energy and Environmental Design (LEED) rating system, in 2010 the U.S. Green Building Council (USGBC) began piloting a new credit to incent demand response efforts in new and existing commercial buildings.

The demand response credit was incorporated into the LEED v4 program (the newest update to the rating system) when adopted by USGBC membership on July 2, 2013,[166] and the LEED v4 program will be fully launched in late 2013.[167]

A facility's eligibility for the credit depends on whether there is an existing demand response program in place or not. For newly constructed facilities in areas with an existing program, credit is given based on several conditions: the capability for real-time, fully automated demand response based on external initiation; an intention to participate in the program for several years; and the ability to reduce peak demand by at least 10 percent. For newly constructed facilities in areas without an existing program, the eligibility requirements include: installing infrastructure to take advantage of future demand response programs or dynamic, real-time pricing programs; developing a plan to shed peak demand by at least 10 percent; and expressing an interest in future program participation to the local utility.[168] Existing commercial buildings can also get credit for participation in demand response programs.

The requirements are similar to newly constructed buildings, with the additional option of getting credit for having a system in place that can permanently shift load from peak to off-peak hours.[169]

(F) Regulatory Barriers to Improved Customer Participation in Demand Response, Peak Reduction, and Critical Period Pricing Programs

The 2009 National Assessment of Demand Response Potential[170] and previous annual reports describe the barriers to customer participation in demand response. The federal government, the Commission, and state and local governments continue to make progress in removing barriers to demand response. Key outstanding barriers and recent actions taken to address these barriers are presented below:

- **Limited Number of Retail Customers on Time-Based Rates.** As noted in past annual reports, greater deployment of time-based rates, while not necessary for the continued development of additional demand response resources, would support the development of new technologies and programs. Projects undertaken by Oklahoma Gas and Electric, Marblehead Municipal Lighting Department and Sioux Valley Energy, and deployed as part of the Recovery Act, are providing new business cases demonstrating that time-based rates can be used to empower consumers and reduce system peak demands.[171] DOE is working closely with these and other recipients of Recovery Act funding to gain further information and insights, particularly in the areas of customer response to dynamic pricing and enabling technologies.
- **Coordination of Federal and State Policies.** A lack of coordination among policies at the federal and state levels could slow the development of demand response resources. Some states have taken action to coordinate state retail demand response programs and policies with organized wholesale markets so that programs at the retail and wholesale level are complementary. For example, the California Energy Commission conducted a workshop with CPUC staff, CAISO and stakeholders to gather input on public policies needed to expand the amount of automated demand response resources available to CAISO.[172] On the other hand, some states have limited retail customers' demand response participation in wholesale markets.
- **Measurement and Cost-Effectiveness of Reductions**. Previous annual reports have described barriers associated with the

measurement and cost-effectiveness of demand reductions. As noted above, the Commission, NAESB, and the National Forum on the National Action Plan on Demand Response undertook steps to address the lack of consistency in the measurement and verification of demand reductions this past year. While providing guidance on measurement and verification methods for market settlement (including design considerations and continuing challenges), the National Forum's Measurement and Verification Working Group identified outstanding issues associated with impact estimations.[173] In addition, the National Forum's Demand Response Cost-Effectiveness Working Group identified a number of additional research topics associated with quantifying program benefits and costs.[174]

- **Lack of Uniform Standards for Communicating Demand Response Pricing, Signals and Usage Information.** Past annual reports have also identified the need for common information models and protocols to promote more efficient transfer of usage and pricing information between parties. Significant progress has been made within the NIST smart grid interoperability framework process with respect to demand response pricing, signals, and usage information. Organizations such as the North American Energy Standards Board, the Organization for Advancement of Structured Information Systems, and the ISO/RTO Council have generated or sponsored work products that offer standardized approaches to retail and wholesale demand response pricing, signals, and usage information. As a result, standards have been written, and some products such as OpenADR 2.0, Smart Energy Profile 2.0, and Green Button are in various stages of adoption for retail and wholesale markets. Other standards, such as those to facilitate two-way power flow to allow plug-in electric vehicles within demand response programs to be used as electric storage and provide ancillary services, will take longer to finalize and perhaps even longer to reach utilities and consumers.
- **Opportunities for Customer Education and Engagement.** Surveys indicate that customer awareness of the smart grid is currently low.[175] The experiences of several utilities demonstrate that successful customer engagement efforts can promote acceptance of smart grid technologies and increase interest in time-based pricing programs.[176] Ongoing research by the Smart Grid Consumer Collaborative is one source for best practices around customer engagement related to the smart grid and time-based pricing programs.[177]

- **Lack of Demand Response Forecasting and Estimation Tools**. The National Action Plan Forum's Estimation Tools and Methods Working Group analyzed and identified gaps between stakeholder's demand response needs (both immediate and anticipated) and the availability of various analytical capabilities, services and tools to meet these demand response needs.[178] The results of their study indicate that existing analytic capabilities and services are sufficient to effectively address many demand response stakeholder needs. However, the Estimation Tools and Methods Working Group identified four areas where further development may be appropriate: (1) End-user settlement tools, (2) load serving entities/electric distribution companies (LSE/EDC) site opportunity assessment tools, (3) LSE/EDC program implementation tools, and (4) LSE/EDC impact assessment tools.

End Notes

[1] Energy Policy Act of 2005, Pub. L. No. 109-58, § 1252(e)(3), 119 Stat. 594 (2005) (EPAct 2005 section 1252(e)(3)).

[2] The Commission submitted the first report, the *Assessment of Demand Response and Advanced Metering: Staff Report*, Docket No. AD06-2, August 7, 2006 (referred to here as the 2006 FERC Demand Response Report), http://www.ferc.gov/industries/electric/indus-act/demand-response.asp. The 2007 through 2012 annual reports are also available at http://www.ferc.gov/industries/electric/indus-act/demand-response.asp.

[3] FERC uses the term advanced meter as synonymous with advanced AMI meters (i.e., smart meters). As defined by the EIA, advanced AMI meters have built-in two-way communication capable of recording and transmitting instantaneous data (measured and recorded usage data at minimum, in hourly intervals, provided to both consumers and energy companies at least once daily). *See* EIA, EIA Form-826 and EIA Form-861 Frequently Asked Questions (FAQs), http://www.eia.gov/survey/faqs/electricity.html.

[4] Energy Information Administration, Form EIA-861, 2011 Data File 2 and File 8, http://www.eia.gov/cneaf/electricity/page/eia861.html.

[5] FERC, *2012 Assessment of Demand Response and Advanced Metering: Staff Report*, December 2012, http://www.ferc.gov/legal/staff-reports/12-20-12-demand-response.pdf.

[6] Institute for Electric Efficiency, *Utility-Scale Smart Meter Deployments, Plans & Proposals*, May 2012, http://www.edisonfoundation.net/iee/Documents/IEE_Smart Meter Rollouts_ 0512.pdf. Penetration rate based on 35.7 million installed advanced meters (IEE) and 151.7 million U.S. electric consumers (Energy Information Administration, Form EIA-861 Data, Data File 2, 2011). IEE predicts that if present trends continue, about 65 million advanced meters will be installed nationwide by 2015.

[7] IEE, *Utility-Scale Smart Meter Deployments: A Foundation for Expanded Grid Benefits*, August 2013, http://www.edisonfoundation.net/iee/Documents/IEE SmartMeterUpdate 0813.pdf.

[8] American Recovery and Reinvestment Act of 2009, Pub. L. No. 111-5 (2009).

[9] U.S. Department of Energy, SmartGrid.gov, "Advanced Metering Infrastructure and Customer Systems, Smart Meters Deployed and Operational," http://www.smartgrid.gov/recovery_act /deployment_status. Note responses were provided by 78 entities. SGIG recipients have reported approximately 15.4 million advanced meters physically installed as of June 30, 2013.

[10] *See* Green Button, "About Green Button," http://www.greenbuttondata.org/greenabout.html.

[11] *Ibid.* Data are available from the date of smart meter installation up to 13 months, or even longer in some cases.

[12] States currently participating include Arkansas, California, Illinois, Indiana, Kentucky, Louisiana, Maryland, Massachusetts, Michigan, North Carolina, Ohio, Oklahoma, Pennsylvania, Tennessee, Texas, Virginia, and West Virginia, as well as the District of Columbia. Green Button, "Adopters," http://www.greenbuttondata.org/greenadopt.html.

[13] NIST webinar, April 2013, http://collaborate.nist.gov/twikisggrid/bin/view/SmartGrid/PAP20 MeetingMinutesAndSlides.

[14] NIST established the Smart Grid Interoperability Panel as a public-private partnership to help manage the development of smart grid interoperability standards in 2010.

[15] SDG&E, "Green Button Connect My Data," http://www.sdge.com/using-green-button-connect-my-data.

[16] Energy Star, "Home Energy Yardstick," https://www.energystar.gov/index.cfm?fuseaction= HOME_ENERGY_YARDSTICK.showGetStarted.

[17] NIST, PAP20 Green Button ESPI Evolution, http://collaborate.nist.gov/twiki-sggrid/bin/view/SmartGrid/GreenButtonESPIEvolution.

[18] Examples include Florida Power & Light, Southern California Edison, and San Diego Gas & Electric.

[19] The GridWise Alliance, *Improving Electric Grid Reliability and Resilience: Lessons Learned from Superstorm Sandy and other Extreme Events*, Workshop Summary and Key Recommendations, June 2013, http://www.gridwise.org/documents/ImprovingElectricGrid ReliabilityandResilience_6_6_13webFINAL.pdf.

[20] Edison Electric Institute, *Before and After the Storm*, January 2013, pp. 1, 7, 12, http://www.eei.org/issuesandpolicy/electricreliability/mutualassistance/Documents/Before% 20and%20After%20the %20Storm.pdf.

[21] Tom Johnson, "Smart Grid, Meters, No Magic Bullet for Damage Done by Major Storms," NJ Spotlight, http://www.njspotlight.com/stories/12/12/03/smart-grid-meters-no-magic-bullet-for-damage-done-bymajor-storms/.

[22] Katherine Tweed, "Smart Grid Saves EPB Chattanooga $1.4M in One Storm," Greentechgrid, October 17, 2012, http://www.greentechmedia.com/articles/read/distribution-automation-saving-epb-millions.

[23] ComEd, "ComEd's 'Smart Switches' Reducing Service Interruptions," April 30, 2013 [Press release], https://www.comed.com/newsroom/news-releases/Pages/newsroomreleases0430 2013. pdf.

[24] Jeannette M. Mills, "Working to put this storm behind us offers glimpse ahead to smarter grid," November 2012, http://www.bge.com/Blog/archive/tags/Smart%20Grid/default.aspx.

[25] Martin LaMonica, "Smart Meters Help Utility Speed Sandy Restoration," MIT Technology Review, October 31, 2012, http://www.technologyreview.com/view/506711/smart-meters-help-utility-speed-sandyrestoration/.

[26] SDG&E, "SDG&E Launches Advanced Outage Management System To Benefit Region," November 12, 2012 [Press release], http://www.sdge.com/newsroom/press-releases/2012-11-14/sdge-launches-advanced-outagemanagement-system-benefit-region.

[27] Katherine Tweed, "SDG&E Pushes the Envelope on Cutting Outages," Greentechgrid, November 21, 2012, http://www.greentechmedia.com/articles/read/sdge-pushes-the-envelope-on-cutting-outages.

[28] For example, the SGIP includes a cybersecurity working group with a subgroup to address privacy issues. The SGIP work on privacy can be found at http://collaborate.nist.gov/twiki-sggrid/bin/view/SmartGrid/CyberSecurityCTG.

[29] State and Local Energy Efficiency Action Network, *A Regulator's Privacy Guide to Third-Party Data Access for Energy Efficiency*, December 18, 2012, http://www1.eere.energy.gov /seeaction/pdfs/cib regulator privacy guide.pdf.

[30] NARUC, *Cybersecurity for State Regulators 2.0*, http://www.naruc.org/grants/Documents /NARUC%20Cybersecurity%20Primer%202.0.pdf.

[31] Public Utilities Commission of Nevada, *Joint Application of the Sierra Pacific Power Company d/b/a NV Energy and Nevada Power Company d/b/a NV Energy for authority to establish and implement three separate trial non-standard metering option riders pursuant to the Order issued in Docket No. 11-10007*, Docket No. 12-05003, Order on Reconsideration, January 9, 2013, http://pucweb1.state.nv.us/PDF/AxImages/DOCKETS_2010_THRU_PRESENT/2012-5/22672.pdf.

[32] Michigan Public Service Commission, *In the matter of the application and request of The Detroit Edison Company seeking approval and authority to implement its proposed Advanced Metering Infrastructure Opt Out Program*, Case No. 17053, May 15, 2013, http://efile.mpsc.state.mi.us/efile/viewcase.php?casenum=17053.

[33] New Hampshire General Court, Bill Status System, Senate Bill No. 266, *AN ACT prohibiting electric utilities from installing and maintaining smart meter gateway devices without the residential or business property owner's consent*, Enacted June 7, 2012, http://www.gencourt.state.nh.us/bill_status/Bill_docket.aspx?lsr=2999&sy=2012&sortoption=&txtsessionyear=201 2&txtbillnumber=SB266.

[34] Naperville Smart Grid Initiative, *Naperville Smart Grid Customer Bill of Rights*, undated, http://www.naperville.il.us/emplibrary/Smart_Grid/NSGI-CBoR-web.pdf.

[35] *Naperville Smart Meter Awareness v. City of Naperville*, Memorandum Opinion and Order, Case No. 1:11-cv-09299, (Illinois Northern District Court, March 22, 2013). Accessed: The Daily Herald, https://www.dailyherald.com/assets/pdf/DA124298323.pdf.

[36] California Public Utilities Commission (CPUC), *Resolution E-4527, Pacific Gas and Electric (PG&E), Southern California Edison (SCE), and San Diego Gas and Electric (SDG&E)*, September 27 2012, http://docs.cpuc.ca.gov/PublishedDocs/Published/G000/M028/K949 /28949960.PDF Note the CPUC resolution directs investor-owned utilities to satisfy the intent and requirements of Ordering Paragraph 11 of the CPUC's *Customer Data Access & Privacy Decision, 11-07-056*, Issued July 28 2011, http://docs.cpuc.ca.gov/WORD_PDF /FINAL_DECISION/140369.pdf.

[37] Connecticut Department of Energy and Environmental Protection, *2013 Connecticut Comprehensive Energy Strategy*, February 19, 2013, http://www.ct.gov/deep/lib/deep /energy/cep/2013_ces_final.pdf.

[38] Illinois Commerce Commission, "ICC Approves New ComEd AMI Schedule for Smart Meters," December 6, 2012 [Press release], http://www.icc.illinois.gov/downloads/public /ComEdAMIorderonrehearingrevise.doc.

[39] Illinois Commerce Commission, "ICC Approves Ameren Illinois Advanced Meter Plan, Schedule," December 7, 2012 [Press release], http://www.icc.illinois.gov/downloads/public /AmerenAMIrehearingedit.doc.

[40] SB 9 was enacted with legislative override of the governor's veto. State of Illinois, 98th General Assembly, Senate Bill 9, http://www.ilga.gov/legislation/BillStatus.asp?Doc Num=0009&GAID=12&DocTypeID=SB&LegID=68374&Sessi onID=85&GA=98&SpecSess=0.

[41] State of Illinois, Energy Infrastructure Modernization Act, Public Act 097-0616, Senate Bill 1652, 97th General Assembly (2011), http://www.ilga.gov/legislation/publicacts/fulltext. asp?Name=097-0616.

[42] Rafael Guerrero, "Lawmakers override Quinn on ComEd veto," *Chicago Tribune*, May 23 2013, http://www.chicagotribune.com/news/local/ct-met-illinois-legislature-com-ed-rate-hike-0523- 20130523,0,5365404.story.

[43] Kentucky Public Service Commission, *Consideration of the Implementation of Smart Grid and Smart Meter Technologies*, Case No. 2012-00428, October 2012, http://psc.ky.gov/PSCSCF/2012%20cases/2012- 00428/20121001 PSC ORDER.pdf.

[44] Kentucky Public Service Commission, *Smart Grids in the Commonwealth of Kentucky: Final Report of the Kentucky Smart Grid Roadmap Initiative*, June 2012, http://energy.ky.gov /generation/Documents/Smart%20Grids%20in%20the%20Commonwealth%20of%20Kentu cky. pdf.

[45] Kentucky Public Service Commission, "PSC Opens Case to Look at Smart Grid and Smart Meters," October 2012 [Press release], http://psc.ky.gov/agencies/psc/press/102012 /1001_r02.PDF.

[46] Kentucky Public Service Commission, *Joint Comments on the Consideration of the Implementation of Smart Grid and Smart Meter Technologies*, KPUC Case No. 2012-00428, May 2013, http://psc.ky.gov/PSCSCF/2012%20cases/2012-00428/20130520_ Joint%20Comments.pdf.

[47] Maine Public Utilities Commission, *2012 Annual Report*, February 2013, http://www.maine. gov/tools/whatsnew/attach.php?id=495712&an=1.

[48] Maine Public Utilities Commission, "MPUC: New Time-Of-Use Prices for CMP Residential and Small Commercial Customers," December 5, 2012, http://www.maine.gov /tools/whatsnew/index.php?topic=pucpressreleases&id=463166&v=article08.

[49] Pennsylvania Public Utilities Commission, *Smart Meter Procurement and Installation Order*, Docket No. M-2009-2092655, December 2012, http://www.puc.pa.gov/filing_resources /issues_laws_regulations/act_129_information/smart_meter_technology_pro curement_and_installation.aspx.

[50] Pennsylvania Public Utilities Commission, *Joint Petition of Metropolitan Edison Company, Pennsylvania Electric Company, Pennsylvania Power Company, and West Penn Power Company*, PPUC Docket No. M-2009-2123950, December 2012, https://www.firstenergy corp.com/content/dam/customer/Customer%20Choice/Files/PA/tariffs/FE%20SMIP%20De ployment%20Plan%20Petition%20-%20Complete.pdf.

[51] Act 129 requires electric utilities to provide access to electronic meter data between customers, designated third parties, and providers of conservation and load management services. Pennsylvania General Assembly, Act 129, 66 Pa. C.S. § 2807(f)(3) (2008), http://www.legis.state.pa.us/WU01/LI/LI/CT/HTM/66/00.028.006.001..HTM.

[52] *See supra* note 50.

[53] Pennsylvania Public Utilities Commission, *PECO Smart Meter Universal Deployment Plan*, PPUC Docket No. M-2009-2123950, January 2013, https://www.peco.com/Customer

Service/RatesandPricing/RateInformation/Documents/PDF/New%20Filings/Petitio n%20-%20PECO%20Phase%20II%20Smart%20Meter%20Plan%20-%20Petition.pdf.

[54] EIA, Form EIA-861 Annual Electric Power Industry Report Instructions, http://www.eia.gov /survey/form/eia_861/instructions.pdf.

[55] EIA, Form EIA-861 data files, http://www.eia.gov/electricity/data/eia861/.

[56] *See infra* pp. 4, 17-18. DADS is a system developed by NERC to collect and analyze semi-annual demand response data from several categories of industry participants. Note that NERC states "issues may be identified that require review and modification of the reported data." NERC data is discussed below.

[57] NERC, *2011 Demand Response Availability Report*, March 2013, p. 12, http://www.nerc.com /docs/pc/dadswg/2011%20DADS%20Report.pdf.

[58] Because the data are taken from different sources, caution must be exercised when making direct comparisons between 2011 and 2012 data.

[59] The megawatts reported here represent the megawatts of demand response "registered" for participation and potential deployment in the relevant markets and programs, e.g., capacity markets, economic- and reliability-based programs.

[60] In general, demand response resource potential is the potential peak reduction attributable to demand response resources participating in a demand response program. Additional information can be obtained from the FERC-731 General Instructions and Information, http://www.ferc.gov/industries/electric/indus-act/demandresponse/2012/instructions.pdf.

[61] Monitoring Analytics, LLC, *State of the Market Report for PJM: Volume 2: Detailed Analysis*, March 14, 2013, http://www.monitoringanalytics.com/reports/PJM_State_of_the_ Market /2012.shtml.

[62] NYISO, "NYISO Meets Record Demand with Balanced Array of Resources," July 22, 2013 [Press release], http://www.nyiso.com/public/webdocs/media_room/press_releases/2013 /NYISO%20Meets%20Record%20Demand%20with%20Balanced%20Array% 20of%20 Resources%20-%2007_22_13%20-%20FINAL.pdf.

[63] NYISO, "Heat Wave Drives Record Electricity Usage in New York," July 19, 2013 [Press release], http://www.nyiso.com/public/webdocs/media_room/press_releases/2013/Heat_ Wave_Drives_Record_Electricity_U sage_in_New_York_07192013.pdf.

[64] NYISO, "NYISO Meets Record Demand with Balanced Array of Resources," July 22, 2013 [Press release], http://www.nyiso.com/public/webdocs/media_room/press_releases/2013 /NYISO%20Meets%20Record%20Demand%20with%20Balanced%20Array%20of%20 Resources%20-%2007_22_13%20-%20FINAL.pdf.

[65] *PJM Estimated Demand Response Activity July 15-19*, 2013, p. 2, http://www.pjm.com /~/media/marketsops/demand-response/pjm-hot-days-report-for-july-15-july-19-2013.ashx.

[66] PJM, Week of July 15th, 2013: PJM RTO Operations & Markets, Markets and Reliability Committee Meeting, August 29, 2013, p. 2,http://www.pjm.com/~/media/committees-groups/committees/mrc/20130829/20130829-item-13-hot-weather-operations-presentation.ashx

[67] PJM, "PJM Meets High Electricity Demand During Unusual Heat Wave," September 12, 2013 [Press release], http://www.pjm.com/~/media/about-pjm/newsroom/2013-releases/20130912-pjm-meets-high-electricitydemand-during-unusual-heat-wave.ashx.

[68] ISO New England, *Weekly Market Summary, July 15-21, 2013*, http://www.iso-ne.com/markets/mkt_anlys_rpts/wkly_mktops_rpts/2013/we_2013_07_21_weekly.pdf.

[69] ISO New England, "ISO New England Requests Voluntary Electricity Conservation," July 16, 2013 [Press release], http://www.isone.com/nwsiss/pr/2013/iso_new_england_ requests_voluntary_electricity_conservation_final.pdf; and "ISO New England Continues

Request for Voluntary Electricity Conservation," July 18, 2013 [Press release], http://www.isone.com/nwsiss/pr/2013/iso-ne_continues_request_for_voluntary_conservation_7.18.13.final.pdf.

[70] CAISO, "Northern California-ONLY *Flex Alert* issued by California ISO as heat wave intensifies," June 30, 2013 [Press release], http://www.caiso.com/Documents/FlexAlert-UrgentConservationNeededNowNorthernCalifornia_July12013.pdf.

[71] CAISO, "Reminder: Day 2 of Flex Alert!" July 2, 2013 [Press release], http://www.caiso.com/Documents/ReminderDay2_FlexAlertJul2_2013.pdf.

[72] California ISO, "Demand Response," Demand response and energy efficiency roadmap workshop, May 13, 2013, http://www.caiso.com/informed/Pages/StakeholderProcesses/DemandResponseInitiative.aspx.

[73] California ISO, *Demand Response and Energy Efficiency Roadmap Draft,* June 12, 2013, http://www.caiso.com/Documents/Draft-ISODemandResponseandEnergyEfficiencyRoadmap.pdf.

[74] *Ibid.*

[75] CAISO intends to work through the California Demand Response Measurement and Evaluation Committee (DRMEC) to clarify and standardize terminology for classifying demand response programs and resources (e.g., load modifying resources and supply resources). The DRMEC, established by the California Public Utilities Commission (CPUC), is comprised of members from the CPUC, the CEC, and a representative from each of the three state investor-owned utilities, and provides oversight of all statewide and non-statewide demand response program evaluations.

[76] CEC, "Lead Commissioner Workshop: Increasing Demand Response Capabilities in California," http://www.energy.ca.gov/2013_energypolicy/documents/2013-06-17_workshop/presentations/.

[77] Heather Sanders, "CEC IEPR Demand Response Workshop," presented at Lead Commissioner Workshop on Increasing Demand Response Capabilities in California, June 17, 2013, http://www.energy.ca.gov/2013_energypolicy/documents/2013-06-17_workshop/presentations/Panel_5/06_SandersISO_presentation_06172013.pdf.

[78] ERCOT, "ERCOT board extends demand response pilot, approves price floor for generators," December 20, 2012 [Press release], http://www.ercot.com/news/press_releases/show/26365.

[79] *Ibid.*

[80] ERCOT, "New pilot program offers incentives to reduce electric use during summer peaks," March 25, 2013 [Press release], http://www.ercot.com/news/press_releases/show/26422.

[81] *Ibid.*

[82] NERC, *2011 Demand Response Availability Report*, March 2013, http://www.nerc.com/docs/pc/dadswg/2011%20DADS%20Report.pdf. *Note*: NERC states "issues may be identified that require review and modification of the reported data."

[83] *Ibid.*, p. 12.

[84] *Ibid.*, p. 24.

[85] *Transmission Planning and Cost Allocation by Transmission Owning and Operating Public Utilities*, Order No. 1000, 136 FERC 61,051, at P 153-154 (2011).

[86] DOE, Office of Electricity Delivery and Energy Reliability (OE), "Interconnection Transmission Planning: Awards," http://energy.gov/oe/downloads/interconnection-transmission-planning-awards.

[87] WECC, "Transmission Expansion Plans," http://www.wecc.biz/committees/BOD/TEPPC/Pages/Plans_Home.aspx.

[88] EIPC, "Phase II SSC Meeting Materials," http://www.eipconline.com/Phase_II_SSC_Meetings.html; and " Phase II Resources," http://www.eipconline.com/Phase_II_Resources.html.

[89] ERCOT, *Long-Term System Assessment for the ERCOT Region*, December 2012, http://www.ercot.com/content/news/presentations/2013/2012%20Long%20Term%20System%20Assessment.pdf; *See also* ERCOT Long-Term Study Task Force, *ERCOT LTS Update*, March 2012, http://www.ercot.com/content/committees/other/lts/keydocs /2012 /LTS Update 4 updated.pdf.

[90] DOE, Office of Electricity Delivery and Energy Reliability (OE), "Learn More About Interconnections," http://energy.gov/oe/recovery-act/recovery-act-interconnection-transmission-planning/learn-more-aboutinterconnections.

[91] State-Provincial Steering Committee (SPSC), "Demand Side Management," http://www.westgov.org/sptsc/site/workgroups/dsmwg.htm.

[92] SPSC, *Memorandum to the Committee on Regional Electric Power Cooperation and the State-Provincial Steering Committee*, October 12, 2012, http://www.westgov.org/wieb /meetings/crepcfall2012/summary.pdf.

[93] Navigant Consulting, Inc, *Assessment of Demand-Side Resources within the Eastern Interconnection*, Prepared for Eastern Interconnection States' Planning Council and National Association of Regulatory Utility Commissioners, March 2013, https://eispctools.anl.gov/documents.

[94] Baek, Y.S., et. al., *Eastern Interconnection Demand Response Potential* (ORNL/TM-2012/303), November 2012, prepared by ORNL, managed by UT-Battelle, LLC for the U.S. DOE (contract DE-AC05- 00OOR22725), http://info.ornl.gov/sites/publications/files/Pub 37931.pdf.

[95] The ERCOT LTS Task Force developed three main scenarios: 1) Business as Usual, 2) Drought, and 3) Environmental and sensitivity cases. All three scenarios include demand response resources and a Business as Usual case will be expanded to include new and emerging technologies. *See* ERCOT Long-Term Study Task Force, *ERCOT LTS Update*, March 2012, http://www.ercot.com/content/committees/other/lts/keydocs/2012/LTS_Update_4_updated.pdf.

[96] *Ibid.*

[97] *Demand Response Compensation in Organized Wholesale Energy Markets*, Order No. 745, 76 Fed. Reg. 16,658 (Mar. 24, 2011), FERC Stats. & Regs. 31,322 (2011), order on reh'g, Order No. 745-A, 137 FERC 61,215 (2011).

[98] *See PJM Interconnection, L.L.C.*, 139 FERC 61,256 (2012) and ISO New England Inc., 138 FERC 61,042 (2012).

[99] *See Midwest Indep. Transmission Sys. Operator, Inc.*, 143 FERC 61,146 (2013) and *California Independent System Operator Corp.*, 144 FERC 61,047 (2013).

[100] *New York Independent System Operator, Inc.*, 143 FERC 61,134 (2013).

[101] *Southwest Power Pool, Inc.,* 138 FERC 61,041 (2012).

[102] *Transmission Planning and Cost Allocation by Transmission Owning and Operating Public Utilities*, Order No. 1000, 136 FERC 61,051 (2011), order on reh'g, Order No. 1000-A, 139 FERC 61,132, order on reh'g, Order No. 1000-B, 141 FERC 61,044 (2012).

[103] FERC, *Standards for Business Practices and Communication Protocols for Public Utilities*, Docket No. RM-05-5-020, Order No. 676-G, February 21, 2013, http://www.ferc.gov /whats-new/comm-meet/2013/022113/E3.pdf.

[104] FERC and DOE, *Implementation Proposal for the National Action Plan on Demand Response,* July 2011, http://www.ferc.gov/legal/staff-reports/07-11-dr-action-plan.pdf.

[105] DOE, "A National Forum on Demand Response: What Remains To Be Done To Achieve Its Potential," http://energy. /state- and- regional- policyassistanc-7.

[106] DOE, Office of Electricity Deliverability and Energy Reliability, *Operations and Maintenance Savings from Advanced Metering Infrastructure – Initial Results*, Smart Grid Investment Grant Program, December 2012, http://www.smartgrid.gov/sites/default/files /doc/files/AMI_OM_report_final_12-13-2012[1].pdf.

[107] DOE, Office of Electricity Deliverability and Energy Reliability, *Application of Automated Controls for Voltage and Reactive Power Management – Initial Results*, Smart Grid Investment Grant Program, December 2012, http://www.smartgrid.gov/sites/default/files /doc /files/VVO%20Report%20-%20Final.pdf.

[108] DOE, Office of Electricity Deliverability and Energy Reliability, *Reliability Improvements from the Application of Distribution Automation Technologies – Initial Results*, Smart Grid Investment Grant Program, December 2012, http://www.smartgrid.gov/sites/default/files /doc/files/Distribution%20Reliability%20Report%20- %20Final.pdf.

[109] SmartGrid.gov, "Smart Grid Demonstration Program," http://www.smartgrid.gov/recovery act /overview/smart_grid_demonstration_program.

[110] The Smart Grid Interoperability Panel was established by the National Institute of Standards and Technology, which is responsible for coordinating the development of a framework to achieve interoperability of smart grid devices and systems, including protocols and model standards for information management.

[111] *See* NIST Smart Grid Collaboration Wiki for Smart Grid Interoperability Standards, "PAP19: Wholesale Demand Response (DR) Communication Protocol," https://collaborate.nist.gov /twikisggrid/bin/view/SmartGrid/PAP19WholesaleDR in the section "PAP19 Artifacts, Output and Next Steps," subsection "Overview."

[112] Modeling is undertaken within the International Electrotechnical Commission's Common Information Model.

[113] DOD, Strategic Environmental Research and Development Program (SERDP) and Environmental Security Technology Certification Program (ESTCP), "New Installation Energy and Water Technology Demonstrations Announced for FY 2013," December 13, 2012 [Press release], http://www.serdp.org/News-and-Events/News-Announcements /Program-News/New-installation-energy-and-water-technology-demonstrations-announced-for-FY-2013.

[114] DOD, SERDP and ESTCP, "Energy," http://www.serdp.org/Program-Areas/Energy-and-Water/Energy.

[115] Jeffrey Marqusee, "The Contribution of Technology to Sustainable Energy Panel Discussion," presented at the 2013 J.B. and Maurice C. Shapiro Conference: Laying the Foundation for a Sustainable Energy Future: Legal and Policy Challenges, George Washington University Law School, April 11, 1013, http://www.law.gwu.edu/News/2012- 2013Events/Pages /LayingtheFoundationforaSustainableEnergyFutureLegalandPolicyChallenges.aspx.

[116] Commander, Navy Installations Command (CNIC), "About Naval District Washington," http://www.cnic.navy.mil/ndw/About/index.htm.

[117] DOD, SERDP and ESTCP, "Demonstrating Enhanced Demand Response Program Participation for Naval District Washington (EW-201343)," http://docs.serdp-estcp.org/Program-Areas/Energy-andWater/Energy/Microgrids-and-Storage/EW-201343/EW-201343/(language)/eng-US.

[118] GSA, "Facilities Management Overview," http://www.gsa.gov/portal/content/104476?utm_ source=PBS&utm_medium=printradio&utm_term=HDR_1_Bldgs_facilities&utm_ campaign=shortcuts.

[119] WorldEnergy, "GSA Awards World Energy 5-Year Energy Management Contract," September 8, 2010 [Press release], http://staging.worldenergy.com/news/gsa-awards-world-energy-5-year-energy-managementcontract/.

[120] WorldEnergy, "Demand Response Auctions help GSA Generate More Competition and Keep More Revenue from Energy Curtailment Participation," March 1, 2012 [Press release], http://www.worldenergy.com/news/demand-response-auctions-help-gsa-generate-more-competition-and-keep-morerevenues/.

[121] State of Arkansas, Regulation of Electric Demand Response Act, SB 795 (2013), http://www.arkleg.state.ar.us/assembly/2013/2013R/Acts/Act1078.pdf.

[122] CEC, "Lead Commissioner Workshop: Increasing Demand Response Capabilities in California," http://www.energywork shop/presentations/.

[123] California Public Utilities Commission, *Order Instituting Rulemaking Regarding Policies and Protocols for Demand Response Load Impact Estimates, Cost-Effectiveness Methodologies, Megawatt Goals and Alignment with California Independent System Operator Market Design Protocols*, Decision 12-11-025, November 29, 2012, http://docs.cpuc.ca.gov /PublishedDocs/Published/G000/M037/K494/37494080.PDF.

[124] The DRMEC is composed of staff from the California Public Utilities Commission, the California Energy Commission, and a representative from each of the investor owned utilities in the state.

[125] Demand Response Measurement and Evaluation Committee, *Process Evaluation Plan, PY 2012-2014*, November 16, 2012, http://www.cpuc.ca.gov/NR/rdonlyres/7222644F-9FE2-44DA-AD27- 09D27313AA82/0/DRMECprocessevaluationplan20122014redacted.pdf.

[126] Demand Response Measurement and Evaluation Committee, "The DRMEC Process Evaluation Plan for 2012-2014," Presented at Fall 2012 Workshop on Non-Impact Studies (San Francisco, CA), December 6, 2012, http://www.cpuc.ca.gov/NR /rdonlyres/0D9CE50F-7C12-4ABD-B027- 5E7DB6878916/0/20122014ProcessEvaluation PlanPowerPoint.pdf.

[127] SCE, "Powering SoCal," http://www.songscommunity.com/.

[128] California Public Utilities Commission, *Decision Approving Demand Response Program Revisions for Years 2013 through 2014*, Decision 13-04-017, April 18, 2013, http://docs. cpuc.ca.gov/PublishedDocs/Published/G000/M064/K206/64206104.PDF.

[129] California Energy Commission, "Energy Commission Approves More Efficient Buildings for California's Future," May 31, 2012 [Press release], http://www.energy /2012_releases/ 2012-05-31_energy_commission_approves_more_efficient_buildings_ nr.html.

[130] California Energy Commission, *Proposed 2013 Energy Efficiency Standards: Title 24, Part 6, and Associated Administrative Regulations in Part 1*, p. 182, http://www.energy.ca.gov /2012publications/CEC-400- 2012-004/CEC-400-2012-004-15DAY.pdf.

[131] Connecticut Department of Energy and Environmental Protection, *2013 Connecticut Comprehensive Energy Strategy*, February 19, 2013, http://www.ct.gov/deep/lib/deep /energy/cep/2013_ces_final.pdf.

[132] Georgia Power, *Electric Service Tariff: Time of Use – Plug-in Electric Vehicle Schedule: 'TOU-PEV-3'*, http://www.georgiapower.com/pricing/files/rates-and-schedules/2.30_tou-pev-3.pdf.

[133] Idaho Public Utilities Commission, *In the Matter of the Application of Idaho Power for Authority to Temporarily Suspend its A/C Cool Credit and Irrigation Peak Rewards Demand Response Programs*, Case No. IPCE-12-29, Order No. 32776, April 2, 2013, http://www.puc.state.id.us.

[134] State of Illinois, Energy Infrastructure Modernization Act, Public Act 097-0616, Senate Bill 1652, 97th General Assembly (2011), http://www.ilga.gov/legislation. asp?Name=097-0616.

[135] Illinois Commerce Commission, *Petition for Approval of Tariffs Implementing ComEd's Proposed Peak Time Rebate Program*, Interim Order, Docket No. 12-0484, February 21, 2013, http://www.icc.illinois.gov/downloads/public/edocket/341974.pdf.

[136] Illinois Power Agency, *2013 Electricity Procurement Plan*, Docket No. 12-0544, April 5, 2013, http://www.icc.illinois.gov/downloads/public/edocket/345814.pdf.

[137] Maine Public Utilities Commission, *Order Designating Standard Offer Provider and Directing Utility to Enter Entitlement Agreements*, Docket Nos. 2012-00456 and 2012-00409, November 7, 2012, http://www.maine.gov/mpuc/electricity/rfps/standard offer/ sosmall0912/docs/cmporder smallMar2013.pdf.

[138] Efficiency Maine Trust, *2012 Annual Report of the Efficiency Maine Trust*, revised February 12, 2013, http://www.efficiencymaine.com/docs/reports/2012-Annual-Report.pdf.

[139] Timmerman, C., "Maryland Smart Grid Update," presented at the 28th Mid-Atlantic Distributed Resources Initiative Working Group meeting, May 7, 2013, http://sites.energetics.com/MADRI/pdfs/may2013/Timmerman.pdf.

[140] SMECO, *Request of Southern Maryland Electric Cooperative, Inc. For Authorization to Proceed With Implementation Of An Advanced Metering Infrastructure System*, Case No. 9294, ML 140535, June 13, 2012, http://webapp.psc.state new.cfm?DirPath= C:\Casenum\9200- 9299\9294\Item_1\&CaseN=9294\Item_1.

[141] Timmerman, C., "Maryland Smart Grid Update," presented at the Mid-Atlantic Distributed Resources Initiative Working Group meeting, May 7, 2013, http://sites.energetics.com /MADRI/pdfs/may2013/Timmerman.pdf.

[142] The EmPOWER Maryland program was established in 2008 upon passage of the EmPOWER Maryland Energy Efficiency Act. The legislation set a goal of reducing per capita electricity consumption and peak demand by 15% by 2015. *See* EmPOWER Maryland Energy Efficiency Act of 2008, 2008 Md. Laws Ch. 131, http://mgaleg.maryland.gov /2008rs/chapters_noln/Ch_131_hb0374E.pdf.

[143] The Maryland Energy Administration's assessment of demand response program performance reflects actual savings from programs implemented from 2007 to 2011 and estimated performance of programs approved through 2015.

[144] Maryland Energy Administration, "EmPOWER Planning Webinar," March 15, 2013, http://energy.maryland.gov/empower3/documents/EmPOWERPlanningWebinar2013-03-15.pdf.

[145] The Dakota Electric Association is an electric distribution cooperative.

[146] Minnesota Public Utilities Commission, *In the Matter of Dakota Electric Association's Petition to Implement an Electric Vehicle Rate*, Order Approving Electric Vehicle Rate As Modified and Requiring Filings, Docket Nos. E-111/M-12-874, November 8, 2012, https://www.edockets.state.mn.us/EFiling/edockets/searchDocuments.do?method=showPoup&documentId={C6A25289-F680-4361-9861-ECC11A1DB71A}&documentTitle=201211-80479-01.

[147] Minnesota Public Utilities Commission, *In the Matter of Minnesota Power's Petition for Approval of a Temporary Rider for Residential Time-of-Day Rate for Participants of the Smart Grid Advanced Metering Infrastructure ("AMI") Pilot Project*, Docket Nos. E-015/M-12-233, November 30, 2012, https://www.edockets.state /edockets /search Documents.do?method=showPoup&documentId={AB400 27B-94DE-49A5-BCA6-883DEDFD7250}&documentTitle=201211-81209-01.

[148] This type of outlet was tested as part of the utility's Residential Small Appliance Pilot Program (RSAP), which ran through the end of 2012. *See* New York Public Service Commission, *Order Adopting Modifications and Tariff Revisions Related to Demand Response Programs*, Case No. 09-E-0115, April 19, 2013, http://www3.dps.ny.gov/W/PSCWeb.nsf/All/A424588D473ED4EF85257687006F3900?OpenDocument.

[149] *Ibid.*

[150] Public Utilities Commission of Ohio, *In the Matter of the Application of Duke Energy Ohio, Inc. for Approval of Pilot Tariff Rate TD 2013*, Case No. 12-3281-EL-ATA, Finding and Order, http://dis.puc.state.oh.us/TiffToPDf/A1001001A13B13B40142J05994.pdf.

[151] Schaefer, "Updates on Advanced Metering Infrastructure (AMI): Ohio Deployments," presented at the 28th Mid-Atlantic Distributed Resources Initiative Working Group meeting, May 7, 2013, http://sites.energetics.com/MADRI/pdfs/may2013/Schaefer.pdf.

[152] Duke Energy Ohio, *Rate TD-13: Optional Time-Of-Day Rate For Residential Service With Advanced Metering (Pilot)*, March 11, 2013, http://www.duke-energy.com/pdfs/Sheet.No.121.RATE.TD-13_3-13.pdf.

[153] AEP Ohio, "gridSMART from AEP Ohio," http://www.gridsmartohio.com/.

[154] AEP Ohio, "Smart Meter Incentive Programs: SMART Shift," https://aepohio.com/save/demoproject/SmartShift.aspx; and "Smart Meter Incentive Programs: SMART Shift Plus," https://aepohio.com/save/demoproject/SmartShiftPlus.aspx.

[155] Pennsylvania Public Utilities Commission, *Energy Efficiency and Conservation Program Implementation Order*, Docket No. M-2008-2069887, January 16, 2009, http://www.puc.pa.gov/electric/pdf/Act129/EEC_Implementation_Order.pdf.

[156] Pennsylvania Public Utilities Commission, *Energy Efficiency and Conservation Program Implementation Order*, Docket Nos. M-2012-2289411 and M-2008-2069887, August 2, 2012, http://www.puc.state.pa.us/pcdocs/1186974.doc.

[157] GDS Associates, *Act 129 Demand Response Study: Final Report*, Prepared for Pennsylvania Public Utility Commission, May 16, 2013, http://www.puc.pa.gov/pcdocs/1230512.docx.

[158] Current tariffs are available at http://www.puc.state/electricity /rates_tariffs/electric_tariffs.aspx.

[159] Matheson, "MADRI Working Group Pennsylvania Update," presented at the 28th Mid-Atlantic Distributed Resources Initiative Working Group meeting, May 7, 2013, http://sites.energetics.com/MADRI/pdfs/may2013/Matheson.pdf.

[160] Rhode Island Public Utilities Commission, *In Re: Narragansett Electric Company d/b/a National Grid's 2012 System Reliability Plan*, Order 20662, Docket No. 4296, February 29, 2012, http://www.ripuc.org/eventsactions/docket/4296-NGrid-Ord20662(2-29-12).pdf.

[161] National Grid, *2012 System Reliability Plan Report – Supplement*, Docket No. 4296, February 1, 2012, http://www.ripuc.org/eventsactions/docket/4296-NGrid-SRP-Supp2012(%202-1-12).pdf.

[162] *Ibid.*

[163] *Ibid.*

[164] Rhode Island Public Utilities Commission, *2013 System Reliability Procurement Report*, Docket No. 4367, November 2, 2012, http://www.ripuc.org/eventsactions/docket/4367-NGrid-SRP-2013Plan(11-2-12).pdf.

[165] Rhode Island Public Utilities Commission, *Re: Narragansett Electric Company d/b/a National Grid's 2013 System Reliability Procurement Plan*, Order No. 20911, Docket Nos. 4366 and 4367, December 21, 2012, http://www.ripuc.org/eventsactions/docket/4366-4367-NGrid-Ord20911(12-21-12).pdf.

[166] U.S. Green Building Council, "USGBC's LEED v4 Passes Ballot and Will Launch This Fall," http://www.usgbc.org/articles/usgbc%E2%80%99s-leed-v4-passes-ballot-and-will-launch-fall.

[167] U.S. Green Building Council, "About LEED v4." http://www.usgbc.org/articles/about-leed-v4.

[168] U.S. Green Building Council, "New Construction, v4 draft: Demand response," http://www.usgbc.org/node/2613001?return=/credits/new-construction/v4-draft.

[169] U.S. Green Building Council, "Existing Buildings, v4 draft: Demand response," http://www.usgbc.org/node/2613007?return=/credits/existing-buildings/v4-draft/energy-%26-atmosphere.

[170] FERC, A National Assessment of Demand Response Potential, June 2009, http://www.ferc.gov/legal/staff-reports/06-09-demand-response.pdf.

[171] DOE, *Demand Reductions from the Application of Advanced Metering Infrastructure, Pricing Programs, and Customer-Based Systems – Initial Results*, SmarGrid Investment Program, December 2012, http://www.smartgrid.gov/sites/default/files/doc/files/peak demand report final 12-13-2012.pdf.

[172] California Energy Commission, "Presentations for June 17, 2013 Lead Commissioner Workshop on Increasing Demand Response Capabilities in California," Docket No. 13-IEP-1F, http://www.energy tations/.

[173] Goldberg, M. and G. K. Agnew, *Measurement and Verification of Demand Response*, February 2013, prepared for the National Forum on the National Action Plan on Demand Response: Measurement and Verification Working Group, http://www.ferc.gov /industries/electric/indus-act/demand-response/dr-potential/napdr-mv.pdf.

[174] Woolf, T., E. Malone, L. Schwartz and J. Shenot, *A Framework for Evaluating the Cost-Effectiveness of Demand Response*, February 2013, prepared for the National Forum on the National Action Plan on Demand Response: Cost-effectiveness Working Group, http://www.ferc.gov/industries/electric/indus-act/demandresponse/dr-potential/napdr-cost-effectiveness.pdf.

[175] Smart Grid Consumer Collaborative, *2013 State of the Consumer Report*, January 21, 2013, http://smartgridcc.org/wp-content/uploads/2013/01/SoCR-2013_1.24.pdf.

[176] Smart Grid Consumer Collaborative, *Smart Grid Consumer Engagement Success Stories*, http://smartgridcc.org/news-events/research-release-sg-customer-engagement-success-stories. *See also* Smart Grid Consumer Collaborative, *2013 State of the Consumer Report*, January 21, 2013, http://smartgridcc.org/wpcontent/uploads/2013/01/SoCR-2013_1.24.pdf.

[177] Consumer engagement is a key topic for the Smart Grid Consumer Collaborative. *See* "Consumer Engagement," http://smartgridcc.org/category/consumer-engagement.

[178] Satchwell, A., C. Goldman, H. Haeri and M. Lesiw, *An Assessment of Analytical Capabilities, Services and Tools for Demand Response*, February 2013, prepared for the National Forum on the National Action Plan on Demand Response: Estimation Tools and Methods Working Group, http://www.ferc.gov/industries/ /napdr-assessment-analytical-tools.pdf.

INDEX

A

B

C

D

E

F

G

H

I

O

P

Q

R

S